The Naked Scientist

The Naked Scientist

The Science of Everyday Life Laid Bare

CHRIS SMITH

Little, Brown

LITTLE, BROWN

First published in Great Britain in 2010 by Little, Brown

A CIP catalogue record for this book
is available from the British Library.

ISBN 978-1-4087-0249-9

re(id
                                                                   ertified
                                                                   ncil.

..., ~~Brown Book Group~~
100 Victoria Embankment
London EC4Y 0DY

An Hachette UK Company
www.hachette.co.uk

www.littlebrown.co.uk

To my wonderful family, Sarah, Amelia, Tim, Jacky and Richard, for making it possible.

And my wonderful friends, Margaret, Tim, Stacey and Robyn, for making it happen.

ACKNOWLEDGEMENTS

As the famous physicist and science populariser Richard Feynman once remarked, 'Science is like sex: sometimes something useful comes out, but that's not the reason we are doing it.'

In other words, science isn't just for stereotypical corduroy-clad geeks and anoraks with shocking teeth, crazy hair and glasses stronger than the Hubble Space Telescope. Instead, it's something that can be hugely fun, affects us all and will almost certainly change your life – whether that means providing the basis for the medical treatment that cures you of a potentially fatal disease, getting you to work safely in the morning, or enabling you to watch England being thrashed in the World Cup in a high-definition, 9.7-gazillion-colour, surround-sound enhanced format on a hundred-inch plasma screen in your living room.

So the goal of this book is to strip down science to the bare essentials and expose you to what it really is – addictively enjoyable, interesting and occasionally a bit naughty. *The Naked Scientist* crystallises all three in this round up of the musings, writings and wider readings of my alter ego, and radio show, of the same name.

When I first went to university in 1993 at the tender age of eighteen, it was to study medicine for five years in order to become a doctor. But five years ultimately turned into eight years when, midway through training, I was bitten by the science bug and decided to do a Ph.D. – on herpes viruses, no less – in the *middle* of my medical degree.

When I emerged from medical school, quite literally as a Dr Dr, I had already begun to dabble with the media. But what really made it possible to translate my love of science and medicine – and my passion for telling people about it – into the world of radio, the Internet, podcasts and even print was the support of some very special people who saw the potential and went far further than the proverbial extra mile to give me the opportunity to develop what has become a major part of my life.

These people deserve enormous thanks and, for this reason, I'd like to acknowledge publicly their friendship and help here. At Cambridge University's pathology department, Stacey Efstathiou (who was a truly excellent Ph.D. supervisor), Tony Minson and Andrew Wyllie have been relentlessly supportive of my work and projects for many years; at the BBC, Howard Benson from 5 Live was instrumental in helping me to get going in mainstream broadcasting, and Tim Bishop and Margaret Hyde helped to ensure that the *Naked Scientists* radio show remains a broadcasting reality across the east of England. At the ABC, in Australia, the Radio National breakfast team, Tim Latham, Steven Turner and Fran Kelly, deserve thanks for creating the radio slot that made me research all the information that's in this book in the first place; and I owe a huge debt of thanks to the Winston Churchill Memorial Trust (WCMT), which made it possible for me to pursue the 'opportunity of a lifetime' and visit Australia for the first time. I also need to say thank you to David Fisher, Lynne Malcolm, Dr Karl and Robyn Williams, all from the ABC, who have taught me so much; Tim Wreghitt from Addenbrooke's Hospital in Cambridge for training me to become a clinical virologist who 'does media' and also encouraging me to write this book; and Tim Whiting and Iain Hunt at Little, Brown, who have been wonderful to work with (and incredibly patient).

The most important thanks of all, however, must go to my wife, Sarah, who has the patience of a saint and somehow puts up with me and the chaotic lifestyle I lead.

Thank you all very much.

Stripping Down Science to the Bare Essentials

Take an onion and chop it finely. Add water, half a pint of washing-up liquid (lemon-scented variety optional) and a handful of salt, and simmer at 60°C (140°F) for ten to twenty minutes. Pour the attractive-smelling mixture through a coffee filter and collect the juice. Cool, add fresh pineapple juice, and incubate at body temperature for ten minutes. Meanwhile, chill some aftershave (that you never liked anyway) in the freezer, and then gently pour twice the volume of ice-cold aftershave over a sample of the onion/pineapple *jus*. Before your eyes, a glutinous blob not dissimilar to snot begins to materialise . . .

This is the recipe for extracting large amounts of DNA from an onion using simple ingredients you can find at home. It's also the recipe that got me started on the radio and led ultimately to my discovery of the most incredible science stories that follow in the pages of this book.

I've always been very keen on science, and particularly on talking to people about it, so when someone emailed me asking if I would be willing to help out at Cambridge University's annual science festival, by giving a talk or demonstrating something suitably scientific, I jumped at the chance.

It was early 1999, I was halfway through my medical degree and Ph.D., and the GM-food debate was in full swing. The letters DNA were emblazoned across every medium; there were newspapers decorated with double helixes – some of which were spiralling the wrong way – and pictures of Frankenstein's monster eating dodgy-looking tomatoes. The general public were terrified that they were about to fall victim to another BSE crisis and shoppers everywhere were eschewing the Jolly Green Giant on the off-chance that he had been much more normally proportioned before someone tinkered with his DNA. But, from talking to people, it was pretty clear that most hadn't got the faintest idea what DNA actually is or even what it looks like, let alone how it works, so this seemed like the perfect opportunity to show them.

In front of the audience who had packed themselves into one of the university's lecture theatres, I set up the onion-DNA demonstration a bit like a cooking programme, inviting volunteers to 'come on down' and help with the procedure. While they vigorously sliced and diced, blinking red-eyed through the onion vapour, I gave a short talk on the nuts and bolts of life's recipe book, including how DNA was discovered, how it copies itself, how it is organised into chromosomes and how it encodes the gene products that do useful things in cells.

The end result was a spectacular handful of snotty onion DNA, a rapt audience for whom I was able to debunk many of the inflammatory molecular myths being peddled by the mass media, and, even more exciting, a phone call from a local commercial radio station, inviting me for an interview the following Thursday.

For moral support, I took along a public-spirited scientific colleague, Shibley Rahman, who is extremely funny and very articulate. Between us we somehow managed to turn what was supposed to have been a five-minute interview about DNA into two hours of light-hearted scientific banter, punctuated by regular music breaks. We must have done something right because the radio station asked us to come back a week later. From there, the concept that became *The Naked Scientists* was born.

Initially we appeared as guests on someone else's programme, but it quite quickly became clear that to realise the true potential of what we wanted to do, we were going to need our own show. As luck would have it, at around the same time one of the UK's mainstream scientific funding bodies, the Biotechnology and Biological Sciences Research Council (BBSRC), unveiled a new scheme to promote 'the public understanding of science' – by getting scientists talking about their subjects – and they were looking for applicants.

3

Thinking, In for a penny, in for a pound, I immediately launched into negotiations with the radio station to buy a year's worth of airtime in order to set up a dedicated one-hour weekly science programme to be broadcast live on a Sunday evening. After some very lengthy discussions – which probably contributed more hot air than the Copenhagen climate summit – we eventually had a deal, but this left the minor matter of how to pay for it. This is where the BBSRC came in. Yet by this time we had just one day left to write and submit the grant application. Shibley suggested we adjourn to the nearest curry house and write the grant proposal over a tandoori and a pint of lager, ostensibly 'to keep our strength up'.

I'm not sure what they put in that curry, but it definitely fired up our writing skills as well as our stomachs, because in January 2000 we were told we'd been successful in our bid, and the show, which was initially christened *ScienceWorld*, was on the road.

I remember the radio station being pretty gobsmacked when I walked in with a cheque the next day, but they duly shifted their Sunday set list around to open up a one-hour slot for us. In the meantime I also signed up another sciencey colleague from Cambridge University, Catherine Hawkins, as a co-presenter alongside Shibley. Together, on 20 February 2000, we took the plunge.

I'm sure we sounded terrible to begin with. The transition from guest to show host is a difficult one. You

4

suddenly have to worry about playing ads and jingles at the correct times, getting the levels right, dealing with live phone calls, while all the time trying to talk intelligently about complicated subjects and keep the conversation going. Although the learning curve was steep, we improved rapidly and before long it was really starting to hang together. We turned the show into a light-hearted look at what was happening each week in the world of science, technology and medicine, and interspersed the chat with popular chart music.

To keep people listening we included a few funny stories – like the one about a Reliant Robin seen parked all over the city of York with an industrial-size sack of potatoes in the passenger seat. It turned out that the driver weighed over 220 kilograms (35 stones) and, without the counterbalancing effect of the potatoes, the three-wheeled car was prone to rolling over on bends. Naturally, we used this story to highlight the importance of eating a balanced diet . . .

The radio station offered us the chance to carry on and make another series of the show after the initial year was up. But, because we all had deadlines looming – including a Ph.D. thesis to complete and clinical finals – we took six months off to get everything finished and to think about how to take the programme forward.

One of the things we had realised during the first series of the show was that, with a live radio programme, if someone missed the show or lived too far away to tune in, there was no prospect of their being able to catch up on the content later. The solution, I felt, was to make use of something that was transforming the way we communicate the whole world over – the Internet. This, I knew, had the potential to deliver a truly global audience, but at very low cost.

At the time, virtually no one was doing anything like this, and certainly not for science radio. I wrote another grant application to the BBSRC asking for support for a further series and also funding to develop a website to act as an online companion to the radio show. The idea was to maximise the reach and educational potential of the material being generated for each show by archiving it in text and audio formats on the web so that anyone, anywhere, any time, could listen to or read it.

We also needed a sexier name, one that clearly defined us as an anorak-free zone, and while I was trying to write a particularly challenging part of my thesis the name 'Naked Scientists' drifted into my head. It seemed like the perfect choice: it was slightly naughty, it made people laugh, it clearly said 'geek-free' – and best of all, the domain name was unclaimed on the Internet!

The BBSRC were kind enough to grant us another year's support so, after my finals, armed with an idiot's guide to HTML, a bottle of beta-blockers, a large jar of coffee and some very late nights, I set up www.thenaked-scientists.com during the two weeks of 'holiday' I had before my new job as a medical doctor began in the late summer of 2001. As a result, when the new *Naked Scientists* radio show hit the airwaves shortly afterwards it also went live across the Internet, becoming in the process one of world's first science podcasts.

This time we focused the show not just on science news stories but around interviews with guest scientists. We signed up a host of well-known luminaries, including evolutionist Richard Dawkins, inventor of genetic fingerprinting Alec Jeffreys, neuroscientist Susan Greenfield, geneticist Steve Jones (who encouragingly told me I share 60 per cent of my genes with a banana), the Astronomer Royal Martin Rees, and even the Nobel laureate DNA pioneer James Watson.

The audience loved it, and not just people listening locally: the website had really taken off. At this stage it was receiving a quarter of a million hits per month – admittedly, many of them on account of the word 'naked', but at least we couldn't be accused of preaching to the converted – and emails were coming in from people all around the world who were enjoying listening to our shows in far-flung corners of the globe.

The competition were also tuning in. The BBC had been listening to us for a while and called up mid-series to invite me over for a 'chat', which culminated in an offer to move the next series of the show to BBC Radio Cambridgeshire. This would see us grow from talking to a few thousand people around the city and outlying villages to talking to a whole county.

By this time it was obvious that we were on to something and that what we were doing had the potential to be much bigger. But I lacked the experience and credibility required to drive a project like this on to greater heights and bigger audiences. By luck rather than judgement I found my way on to the website of the Australian Broadcasting Corporation (ABC), and from there came across the work of someone who I later realised is undeniably one of the best science-radio presenters in the business, Robyn Williams (whose other claim to fame is as an extra in *Monty Python* and *Dr Who* many moons ago).

I wrote a brief email introducing myself and explaining what I was trying to do, but didn't really expect to hear anything back. But I received a call from Australia saying that Robyn Williams was in London for a conference and was willing to meet me. I remember being intensely excited, and also quite nervous, because I had a feeling this was going to be an incredibly important encounter. I needn't have worried. Waiting for me in his hotel's foyer, smiling broadly, was a middle-aged chap in full Aussie regalia, including the shorts and sandals – it was clear that Robyn, having not lived in London for many years, had overlooked the exigencies of the English weather.

Robyn immediately offered to arrange for me to go to Sydney to join the ABC Radio National Science Unit for a spell in 2004. The only thing missing was the minor matter of money and sponsorship. Fortunately, there is a wonderful organisation called the Winston Churchill Memorial Trust (www.wcmt.org.uk), which was established as a living memory to Winston Churchill and offers 'the opportunity of a lifetime' to successful applicants who want to do something 'life-changing'.

In late 2002 I applied to the Churchill Trust, asking them to support a period of six months at the ABC Science Unit. I was interviewed by a panel comprising four of the trust's 'greats', who included the neurologist Dr Roger Bannister, the runner of the world's first four-minute mile. To say the twenty-minute grilling they gave me was 'testing' would be like describing a tornado as 'windy'; but the panel was obviously satisfied that my bid to go to Sydney really was the opportunity of a lifetime and, crucially, would also benefit Britain (the other major criterion for winning an award), because I received a letter shortly afterwards to say that I had been awarded a prestigious Churchill Fellowship.

As I was the only person from my home county (Essex) to win one of the fellowships that year, the trust's press release of successful applicants was picked up by BBC Essex, who invited me along to take part in *Tea at Three with Steve*, one of their afternoon talk programmes. While I was there I also took the opportunity to play some of our previous shows to the BBC Essex director of programming, Tim Gillett. Two days later he phoned to say that, when the new series started on the

BBC in Cambridge, they would like to broadcast it simultaneously on BBC Essex, potentially tripling our audience. Furthermore he wondered whether, in the meantime, I would like to make some special two-hour-long bank-holiday programmes for them?

The prospect of running a two-hour live science show, on an untried audience, at peak time, at a radio station I'd visited only once and using equipment I didn't have the foggiest idea how to operate, was trouser-soilingly scary. It was like being asked to take a Formula One car for a spin having just passed your test in an Austin Allegro. But then there's always been a part of me that just cannot resist a challenge so, terrified as I was, I heard myself saying, 'That'll be wonderful, thank you.'

Mercifully, my fears evaporated when those shows were broadcast in May and August 2003. They drew an enormous audience response: people of all ages from nine to ninety phoned in with questions like 'How many pieces of toast can you make with the energy in a lightning bolt?', 'Why does my car do eight miles to the gallon more with an air filter full of mothballs?' and 'How many organs can I donate and still remain alive?'

With the BBC relaunch we introduced a few changes. I found some fresh talent to join our team in the form of Helen Hendry (now Scales) and Kat Arney, two Cambridge University scientists with appetites and aptitudes for science communication. Kat certainly knew how to make an impact. During her first visit to the programme she managed to conceal her mobile phone in the deepest, darkest, most inaccessible recess of her bag, from where it proceeded to ring, loudly, several times during a live broadcast. I'm not sure what perturbed listeners more, the interruption or her shocking choice of ringtone. I for one honestly didn't have Kat down as a Bros fan.

The other major modification we made was to switch the programme to an all-talk format. Previously we'd interwoven music with the science, usually to cover up our own ineptitude, but this made it difficult to publish the programme on the Internet because, for copyright reasons, we had to edit out all the music. Apart from making extra work, this left the programme sounding fragmented and also ate up airtime that we realised we could put to much better use. Instead, we began to focus heavily on science news items, answering more listeners' questions and featuring interviews with live studio guests who had interesting scientific stories to tell. The results were spectacular: we picked up listeners all over the world, including Australia, Canada, California, even Japan.

After six months we took a break while I headed off to Sydney to join the ABC in early 2004. The ABC threw me in at the deep end. I began making reports for Robyn Williams' *Science Show*, including an interview with the Danish developers of a strain of landmine-locating GM cress plants that turned red when they grew on top of buried ordnance. I also covered a story on *Bdellovibrio*,

the bacterial equivalent of a body snatcher. These predatory organisms invade other microbes and multiply
inside them before finally bursting out to hunt down
fresh victims. Scientists think they might hold the key to
a fresh selection of antibiotic ideas.

Compiling these pieces was a tremendous learning
experience. Members of the ABC science team would
listen and then offer some good-natured, typically
Australian constructive criticism, which usually went
something like 'That sounds like it was recorded in a
toilet. Are you honestly going to broadcast that s**t?'

Just before I returned home to the UK, I encountered
another science-broadcasting icon in the form of Karl
Kruszelnicki, or 'Dr Karl', as he's known to his listeners.
Originally a medical doctor like me, Karl has since
swapped a scalpel for a microphone and is one of
Australia's leading science popularisers. Dubbed 'an
answer in search of a question', he's written at least
twenty-seven science books and appears on national
radio every week to answer listeners' queries on all
things scientific, but in an intensely humorous and
engaging way. Testimony to this is his having won, in
2002, an Ig Nobel prize for the world's first rational
analysis of the colour of belly-button fluff.

Decked out in one of his trademark flamboyant shirts,
Karl invited me to join him on some of his broadcasts,
including talking with Radio 5 Live in the UK. It was
certainly strange to be broadcasting to my own country

from the other side of the world, but it came about because Karl contributes a weekly one-hour science phone-in show, from Sydney, for 5 Live.

I left Australia with something of a heavy heart (because I knew the weather back home wouldn't be a patch on Sydney sunshine) in July 2004. But at the same time I was fired with enthusiasm and a whole lot better equipped to begin creating the kinds of programmes that I felt we needed to be making. After regrouping the *Naked Scientists* presenting team, we set about getting the show back on the road.

At the ABC I learned that doing these things well takes teamwork, but until that time, when it came to the nuts and bolts of producing programmes, identifying and booking guests, publishing podcasts and writing web pages, I had been pretty much a team of one. Realising that my working pattern was probably not compatible with life much beyond the age of forty, I set about looking for a way to get some help.

Thankfully, the Wellcome Trust came to the rescue. They are the UK's largest independent grant-awarding body, giving away over £600 million in research funding every year. One of the areas they also support is science communication. With the help of my boss at Cambridge University, Stacey Efstathiou, I wrote an application to the Wellcome asking them for some serious funding to take on some staff and to launch *The*

Naked Scientists properly, with a major radio and web presence. Daring (and pricey) as that bid was, the Wellcome went for it and agreed to help out.

It was as we were gearing up to do this in 2005 that Apple's iTunes platform announced they were going to be opening up their online music store to include podcasts. Realising that this could have a huge impact on our ability to reach a global audience, I took a day off work and sat in my living room, working out how to rewrite the RSS feeds that served up our podcasts to the world so that they would be iTunes-compatible. It wasn't easy; the instructions Apple had initially circulated seemed to have been written in a language originating from outer space. But somehow I made it work and, looking back, that day arguably ranks as one of the most important things I ever did in the history of *The Naked Scientists*.

In fact, things went so well that the ensuing demand for our content actually blew the top off the processor in our web server! This, an iTunes staff member has subsequently informed me, happened to many others around the world at this time and became known as 'the iTunes effect'. It occurred because, literally overnight, we went from seeing a few thousand downloads of our programmes every month to receiving tens of thousands of download requests per *day*. The bills for the Internet bandwidth were eye-watering, but it was money well spent because, while most people were struggling to find their feet in this new audio arena and were making one or two shows a month, we were pumping out several studio-quality programmes per week, albeit from our back catalogue, as we prepared to launch the new *Naked Scientists* series on the radio. Consequently, and aided by being one of the few science podcasts around at that time, we secured a huge swath of loyal listeners, who in turn spread the word and helped us to sign up even bigger audiences internationally.

We ended up topping the charts in the iTunes stores of most countries, and suddenly what had been a small-scale local radio programme from one tiny corner of the UK now had a global following, with listeners in all four corners of the earth. With it came an inbox-busting torrent of emails from listeners far and wide containing ideas for programme topics, feedback, interesting science stories and questions on every subject under the sun. One Australian researcher wrote in to say that he usually listened to the programme as a boredom-antidote while he dissected the prostate glands of fruit flies! Another listener, a teacher, said he was frequently setting our programmes as homework for his class, which perhaps goes some way to explaining why educational standards are falling . . .

It was this particular communication that got me wondering whether we could take *The Naked Scientists* a step further than a radio programme and podcast. What if we were to introduce a practical, hands-on experimental component to the broadcast? Could this be the way to produce a programme with simultaneous appeal to both adults and younger people? The answer, it turned out, was yes, which is how Kitchen Science was born.

The idea was to design a series of experiments that audience members could try out at home while listening to the show; these would make use of simple ingredients and apparatus, which could be located with only a modest amount of cupboard-emptying or larder-raiding. And, most importantly, by making the experiments relevant to the subject matter of each programme, we could add a visual component to the traditionally non-visual medium of radio, making it much easier to convey some of the more complex concepts we wanted to communicate.

When I told the members of the team that we were going to be designing experiments that we would then encourage the general public to try at home, they all looked horrified; one even picked up the phone to their lawyer! Fortunately I knew of a Cambridge-based physicist, Dave Ansell, who was beginning to carve a career for himself as a successful designer of interactive science experiments and demonstrations. Somehow, Dave let himself be persuaded to join *The Naked Scientists*, and he immediately became the King of Kitchen Science.

Each week we researched, designed and built a

suitable hands-on activity that we would include in the show and then ask listeners to attempt to replicate, inviting them to call in live with their results, which we broadcast.

It was an instant sensation. We had listeners everywhere making their own butter, producing clouds in drink bottles, making fireworks from crisp packets, and even measuring the speed of light in their microwaves. In one experiment, designed to demonstrate why you can nonetheless *see* a transparent object like glass, one young boy phoned in, having filled a large Pyrex bowl with cooking oil and immersed a smaller bowl inside it, to say: 'I've got a huge oily mess in my kitchen, and now my mum's gone really mad, but I guess that's not the observation I was supposed to make!'

On another occasion, an elderly couple called in after we suggested listeners hang an oven shelf from two pieces of string, wrap the string around their index fingers, insert their fingers into their ears and then get a co-experimenter to hit the shelf with a large object. 'It sounds like Big Ben going off in your head,' shouted the now clearly deaf amateur experimenter on the other end of the phone. Meanwhile, in the background, a cacophony of crashes and bangs was audible before a man's voice could be heard saying, 'Come on, love, get off the phone, I'm having trouble hitting this thing on my own . . .'

Realising that there was clearly some fun to be had

17

with this, we also set out to test some slightly more unusual notions. Armed with a helium-powered rifle, a supply of ball-bearing bullets, a gelatin-filled tube of Perspex to mimic adipose tissue and a camera capable of taking over a thousand images per second, we successfully measured how fat you would have to be to fend off a bullet travelling at over 1200 miles per hour using just your belly. The answer, at a lardaceous 76 cm of flab out front, argues that you'd be dead from heart disease long before any bullet got within a mile of you! However, the result was also a fatal body blow for our web server, which was crippled as a million people planet-wide simultaneously tried to log on to watch the footage of the experiment taking place. Needless to say, we didn't encourage the audience to try that particular experiment at home – either the shooting bit or the weight-gain aspect – although some listeners did write in to say that, fired with enthusiasm by our broadcast, they were now working harder than ever to improve their personal 'body armour' by doubling their portion sizes . . . Oops; there goes the public health message.

But it wasn't all just hard work and physics. Recognising that tea breaks are important too, we decided to carry out the world's first objective, scientific appraisal of the acclaimed uselessness of a chocolate teapot, which, in fact, turns out to be a myth: a chocolate teapot, we found, can actually produce a pretty pleasant brew.

To make the teapot, we first needed to know what thickness of chocolate would be required. We filled sections of Perspex drainpipe with different depths of molten chocolate. Once it had set into a hard plug, we added boiling water and timed how long it took before the chocolate melted out. These experiments showed that a layer of chocolate about an inch thick could withstand the effects of the boiling water without melting through. This meant that, to make an actual teapot, we were going to need nearly two kilograms of Bournville. This was obtained by emptying the entire shelf of chocolate in our local shop, the proprietor of which then asked if we wanted any insulin as well, pointing out that there was a chemist next door.

The chocolate was melted and then 'cast' using two glass bowls, one placed inside the other, as a mould. We drilled a hole in one side and assembled and attached a spout, producing a slightly rough but none the less functional teapot, capable of brewing a perfectly palatable, if slightly sweet, cup of Earl Grey for the *Naked Scientists* team.

Experiments like these helped to reinforce our 'science with a sense of humour' motto. They also helped to attract legions of loyal fans to the radio programmes, podcasts and website. In fact, the material became sufficiently popular that, before long, we were regularly serving up over ten terabytes of programme downloads and web pages every month. Unfortunately, the organisation with whom our site was hosted was not altogether pleased at the pressure being applied to their network by our popularity. They told me, in no uncertain terms, to leave, giving us just fourteen days to exit our 'e-premises' before they pulled the plug.

Victims of our own success, and with just a fortnight to find the website a new home that could take the strain, we began the mammoth task of phoning every Internet hosting company we could find in the UK. A predictable pattern to the conversations soon emerged:

Them: So what are you looking for?

Me: Well, we run a website and we do a bit of podcasting.

Them: So how much traffic do you get?

Me: Oh, it's not much.

Them: Well, how many hits a day, for example?

Me: Erm, not a lot really. A million or so.

Them: A million hits a day!

Me: Is that a lot then?

Them: Well, how much bandwidth are you using?

Me: Er, about ten terabytes a month. It's not a lot really . . .

At this point the phone would usually go silent for a moment before a slightly incredulous voice would inform me that I was clearly insane and they couldn't help; or there would be the sound of frenzied tapping on a calculator, followed by a price so large that it had to be expressed in standard form!

We were almost out of options. There was one company left: they were based in Manchester and their website informed me that they were the UK's 'best hosting provider'. Nervously I picked up the phone, but this time things went differently. Rather than suggesting a trip to the nearest padded cell, the person who answered said, 'You need to talk to my boss,' and immediately connected me to one of the company directors.

He listened patiently while I explained that we were about to be evicted by our present web hosts, and that we were also penniless. Would he consider sponsoring us, in return for promotional coverage in our programmes and on our website? 'Leave it with me,' he said, uttering the phrase any salesman dreads. But true to his word he phoned back two days later and invited me to meet with him and the company's founder and managing director at an Internet trade fair in London.

He was sufficiently intrigued by what we were doing, and its value to society, that he immediately offered to help, and our project was saved. There and then we had a new home for our website and podcast and two very good new friends. And now, over four years later, the company, UKFast, is still supporting us.

In the meantime we've also diversified what we do on the radio quite considerably. A chance encounter with a producer from South Africa's hugely popular Johannesburg-based Talk Radio 702 led to the creation of a *Naked Scientists* weekly slot on the station every Friday morning, featuring me live from my living room. Partly as a result of the success of this show, our entire team was invited to take part in the 2009 SciFest, South Africa's annual science festival, in Grahamstown, the home of Rhodes University, in the Eastern Cape. They wanted a series of one-hour science-based stage shows that would entertain and educate young people.

We were thinking that we'd probably be presenting to a crowd of maybe a hundred or so people at a time, in fairly intimate surroundings, and we could probably therefore get away with a collection of fairly small-scale hands-on-type experiments. But then, about three weeks before we were due to fly out, a large pack of instructions and briefing notes arrived. We were scheduled, it said, to appear on five successive days in the main auditorium – which seated a thousand people. And they'd sold all the tickets. Ouch.

This provoked a rapid rethink and some even faster experimental development and design. Pulling a few all-nighters, Dave Ansell built a gherkinator – literally an electric chair for gherkins – so we could plug pickles into the mains to make them glow orange; we developed a way to make polycarbonate bottles explode spectacularly when filled with liquid nitrogen; we turned a vacuum cleaner into a bazooka; used a toaster to power a hot air balloon; and I came up with a few experiments involving hydrogen-powered rockets and methane-filled snakes.

We had just one day to rig up and rehearse after we arrived. None the less, the house was packed and the roar from the crowd of ten- to thirteen-year-olds when we walked on nearly blew us over. But not quite as nearly as one of the experiments.

We were demonstrating how gases burn by igniting balloons filled with hydrogen, which make a satisfying *boom* when they ignite. But because we figured it was a large auditorium and the audience wanted to see some exciting stuff, I also rigged up a balloon containing a mixture of hydrogen *and* oxygen. When this mixture is lit, it should detonate with a much louder bang, because the reaction happens much more quickly. So you can imagine our disappointment when, having talked this up before an expectant audience, I held a lit taper up to the balloon and it just went *pop*. The taper had gone out just before it got to the balloon, so the sharp end of the extinguished taper just burst the balloon. Realising this, Ben Valsler, the other presenter in our team, moved on to a different experiment while I went backstage to rig up another balloon.

I'm not really sure how I did it, but this time I must have got the mixture of gases absolutely right for the reaction to work perfectly. I was probably also a bit more generous with the amounts I put in. Anyway, I went back on the stage, apologised for the previous misfire, and recued the audience. As I donned my ear defenders I warned them that it might be a bit noisy – which turned out to be the understatement of the century.

To say that the ensuing blast was loud would be like calling a nuclear weapon a small firework. The shockwave was devastating. It literally blew me backwards, destroyed several normal air-filled balloons that were sitting on a table a metre or two away, and filled the air in front of the stage with the dusty remnants of a balloon that appeared to have been ripped apart at the molecular level, quite possibly also creating a simultaneous rift in the space–time continuum.

The audience were momentarily stunned into silence and, for a few seconds, the loud cheering and clapping that had pervaded the rest of the show was replaced by a strange serenity, and a cloud descending from the ceiling as decades of accumulated dust, dislodged by the blast, began to drift floorwards. Then everyone went wild, making a noise almost as loud as the blast, crying, 'Do it *again*!'

And do it again we did, five times in Grahamstown followed by another four shows in Cape Town. It was both exhilarating and, at the same time, a truly humbling experience to meet young people who had in some cases travelled for more than thirteen hours in a minibus to come to see our shows.

I'm still incredulous and delighted that something that started out over ten years ago as a fun DNA-based demonstration for a science festival has turned into a global sensation that has now won seven national and international communication and broadcasting awards. Most importantly, none of it would have been possible without the incredible and loyal team of people who have been part of it and supported it over the years, including Dave Ansell, Ben Valsler, Meera Senthilingam, Diana O'Carroll, Helen Scales and Kat Arney; in my view, the best bunch of broadcasters there is.

And in case anyone's curious, there's sufficient energy in a lightning bolt to make more than a hundred thousand pieces of toast. And you can donate eight organs, or segments of organs, and still remain viable; they are a lung, a liver lobe, a segment of pancreas, a section of bowel, a kidney, some skin, some bone marrow and (for the ultra-altruistic) your corneas.

Read on . . .

Spot the ball

It's official: we mustn't blame the goalie (or at least, not always) for letting in a curling shot – scientists have proved that the brain just cannot process the trajectory of spinning balls.

Psychologist Cathy Craig from Queen's University, Belfast, first began studying the problem after watching footballer Roberto Carlos score for Brazil in 1997. 'Everybody thought it was going wide, but it curved in at the last minute,' she said. To investigate why even professionals seem so poor at predicting where the curling ball will end up, she asked players to predict where it would go in a series of virtual-reality shots on a display screen. The ball viewed by participants had an added spin of six hundred revolutions per minute. The result, she found, was that even the pros were unable to predict the path that the ball would take correctly.

A spinning ball generates an effect called the Magnus force, which causes it to follow a curved path, especially as it slows down. But because such an effect doesn't occur in nature, we haven't evolved a visual mechanism to process it, as we have for anticipating the effects of gravity. So it seems the keeper's off the hook – for *those* misses, anyway . . .

Is it really possible to read other people like a book?

With the advent of the Internet, and access to the latest learning just a few button-pushes away from the average living room, what's the role of the library? Well, in place of books, perhaps the future lies in lending out people. Based on a concept conceived originally in Denmark and dubbed the 'Human Library', a number of institutions across Europe and farther afield are taking the unusual step of adding humans to their archives, including gypsies, journalists, lesbians and animal-rights activists. 'Readers' pop into the library and borrow the individual for a half-hour chat in a nearby café about their life, beliefs and values. Apparently, the main idea is to let people come face to face with their prejudices, although an additional bonus is that the 'books' find their way back to the library on their own afterwards, saving you having to return them.

FACTOID:

*'Sound travels twice as fast in air
as it does in water.'*

FALSE

Sound waves actually travel four times *slower* in air
than in water.

What's worse – to wake up to an alarm clock or to replace one you've smashed?

Are you one of those people with an alarm-clock allergy or a penchant for the snooze button? Massachusetts Institute of Technology's Media Lab think they might have the answer to your bed-loving tendencies with 'Clocky', an alarm clock on wheels that runs off! As soon as you hit the snooze button to silence Clocky, he zooms off to a random hiding-place elsewhere in the room, forcing you to get up and find him to shut him up. The ensuing hunt should provoke even the most bed-fast individual to eschew the sheets and head for the shower.

So romantic to have a quiet drink together – but what if we are far apart?

Absence makes the heart grow fonder, and now a pair of Wi-Fi drinking glasses could help to bring separated loved ones closer together, according to researchers at MIT's Media Lab. Inventors Jackie Lee and Hyemin Chung have incorporated a variety of coloured LEDs, liquid sensors and Wi-Fi links into a pair of tallish tumblers. When one drinker picks up his or her glass, red LEDs in the partner's glass switch on, and when one of the pair puts a glass to his or her lips, white LEDs glow around the rim of the other glass, showing that the partner has taken a sip. The inventors claim that their wireless glasses help people feel that they're sharing an intimate drinking experience together, even when one of them is on the other side of the world.

More practically, the technology could also prove useful in the setting of a hospital or a care institution to check that patients or elderly and infirm people are drinking enough water, for example. The 'lovers' cups', as they have been christened, were unveiled at the Montreal CHI 2006 Conference on Computer–Human Interaction.

Greenhouse gases a breath of fresh air

A whiff of methane has helped Japanese researchers to sniff out signs of Earth's earliest life using rock samples from western Australia. Yuichiro Ueno and his colleagues at the Tokyo Institute of Technology studied samples of quartz collected from a geological feature called the Dresser Formation, which dates back about 3.5 billion years and consists of pillows of lava containing vertical quartz seams topped by sedimentary rocks. Under a microscope the quartz turns out to be stuffed with tiny time-capsules, in the form of bubbles of water and gas trapped when the rocks were first deposited. By crushing them open, the Japanese team was able to collect and analyse the ancient gases and, by studying their chemical composition, find out where they came from.

Their results show that the bubbles contain a lot of methane that bears the chemical signature of life, indicating that some of Earth's earliest inhabitants were methane-producing microbes. Specifically, the methane the researchers found is in a form referred to as '13C-depleted', which is a hallmark of life because micro-organisms are known to be fussy and prefer to use the lighter carbon-12 (12C) isotope. So we now know that some of the earliest organisms flourishing on

31

Earth were producers of the greenhouse gas methane, and researchers think they may have made a big contribution to keeping the planet warm, because in those days the sun emitted less heat energy than it does today.

Can we immunise against MS?

Researchers in the US have come up with a novel way to tackle the debilitating neurological disease multiple sclerosis (MS). In patients with the disease, the immune system mounts an attack on a substance in the brain called myelin, which covers and encloses nerve fibres – rather like the insulating material surrounding an electrical cable. Damage to this myelin coat prevents affected nerve fibres from transmitting information correctly, which causes sufferers to develop problems with their vision, speech, sensation and movements. This damaging immune attack is driven by a specific population of renegade white blood cells known as autoreactive T cells. Suppressing the immune system with drugs can help to damp down the activity of these rogue cells, but putting anything other than a temporary stop to their terroristic tendencies has proved impossible.

But now researchers have found that the cells may hold the key to their own undoing – by turning them into a vaccine, which has been named Tovaxin®. Texas-based Opexa Therapeutics have shown that if samples of the myelin-attacking T cells are collected from the blood of an MS patient, damaged with a dose of radiation to stop them from growing, and then reinjected, the patient's immune system can be trained to recognise the defective cells and kill others like them, stopping the MS in its tracks.

In an initial trial involving fifteen MS patients who received the new treatment, the rate of flare-ups of their disease was reduced by 92 per cent. In a subsequent larger study involving 150 patients that was completed in late 2008, Tovaxin treatment resulted in a relapse rate of less than 20 per cent, which is at least as good as the best drug currently on the market. Better still, 16 per cent of the Tovaxin-treated patients exhibited sustained improvements in their neurological symptoms, suggesting that the brain is capable of repairing some of the damage, so long as the disease remains inactive. Researchers are, however, interpreting the results with caution, because no vaccines yet produced have been shown to modify the ultimate course of MS successfully. In other words, more time will be needed to find out whether the benefits of Tovaxin are long-lived.

A hands-on approach to fingerprinting

Researchers have come up with a novel way to lift finger-prints non-destructively from a variety of previously 'un-fingerprintable' surfaces – like skin – by using X-rays. The approach relies on the detection of the salts that are present in sweat and which are deposited in trace amounts when a surface is touched, leaving a salty fingerprint-impression. The X-rays excite the salt atoms, making them produce a characteristic light of their own, which can be picked up by a detector.

Apart from fingerprints, the new approach can also pick up other chemical signatures present at a crime scene, including, for instance, gunpowder or explosives, which can provide extra evidence about the activities of the culprit.

Making life a smell of a lot better for people downwind of a pig farm

Researchers George Preti and Charles Wysocki, from Philadelphia's Monell Chemical Senses Center, have hit upon a way to make the lives of people who live near farms more bearable at times of the year when farmers fertilise their land the natural way. They have come up with a chemical that makes you think that manure smells nice!

It's been known for some time that when an odour is present for a long period of time the nose learns to ignore it, a process called 'adaptation'. But certain chemicals can fool the nose into ignoring other smells too, which is known as 'cross-adaptation', and this is the approach taken by the Monell scientists. They first tracked down the identity of the molecules that make manure hard to live with, and then set about testing pleasant-smelling chemicals to find examples capable of 'blinding' the nose to the *bouquet d'ordure*. They eventually tracked down the perfect example – the ethyl-ester of 3-methyl-2-octanoic acid – which, when added to manure, can counteract its odour. Naturally, the smell still reaches your nose, but you just don't notice it. If combined with other odour-combating chemicals, say the scientists, it could make a smell of a difference to life downwind of a farm at fertilising time.

How does an embryo tell its arse from its elbow, or at least where to produce a placenta?

One finding that might help to explain why cloning remains a highly hit-and-miss affair has been produced by a team of scientists at the University of Missouri, Columbia. They have pinpointed how a developing embryo, a pinhead-sized structure consisting of a ball of similar-looking cells, determines which of these cells will become the foetus, and which will form the placental lifeline linking the baby to its mother. By studying fertilised mouse eggs, Michael Roberts and his team found that when the egg divides for the first time, the products of a gene called Cdx2 make their way to the nucleus, where the DNA is located, in just *one* of the two cells. As the embryo develops, this cell and its descendants go on to give rise to the placenta and umbilical cord, whereas the other cell, without any Cdx2 in its nucleus, forms the baby. To prove that they were on the right track, the researchers injected the cells containing Cdx2 with substances that could stop the gene from operating. Embryos treated in this way failed to produce a placenta.

The team also found that, in unfertilised eggs, the products of the Cdx2 gene were preferentially localised on just one side of each egg, so that when an egg was fertilised and began to divide, one of the daughter cells inherited the Cdx2 products and the other did not. This finding turns on its head our traditional belief that, at early stages at least, all the cells in an embryo are equal, and may help to improve the efficiency of current cloning techniques.

Reading writing lost for centuries

The Archimedes Palimpsest is the oldest surviving transcript of the work of the ancient Greek mathematician Archimedes. It was laboriously copied out as a manuscript in the tenth century but unfortunately during the twelfth century a pious owner recycled it into a prayer book by scraping off the ink and replacing maths with miracles! Luckily, thanks to modern technology it is now possible to read it again, almost a thousand years later, with the help of X-rays. Scientists at the Stanford Synchrotron radiation laboratory in California used a beam of concentrated X-rays produced by a particle accelerator to see through the prayers, plus some twentieth-century repair work, to disclose the original mathematical marvels hidden beneath. The technique works by exciting iron atoms in remnants of the original ink, causing them to glow and create a sharp image which the researchers can read.

FACTOID:

'Chalk in cliffs like the White Cliffs of Dover is made up of the fossils of tiny animals.'

FALSE

The chalk is made up of the calcium carbonate shells that tiny animals called cocolithophores accreted around themselves when they lived in the sea seventy million years ago during the cretaceous period. On the death of a cocolithophore, its shell would disintegrate into separate chalky discs, and sink to become part of the sediment on the seabed.

TECHNOLOGY

A wearable way to pick up signs of boredom

Researchers at the MIT Media Lab are developing a mobile boredom detector designed to clip on to a pair of glasses and warn wearers if they are sending the people they meet to sleep. The device is the brainchild of

MIT's Rana El Kaliouby, who hopes in particular that it will make life easier for people with conditions like Asperger's or autism, which can make it difficult for sufferers to interpret the body language of others. It works by relaying images of the facial expressions made by people chatting to the wearer to a hand-held computer, which analyses the pictures and picks out how the individual is responding to the conversation. Specifically, the software focuses on movements of the eyebrows, lips and nose, and also tracks nods and shakes of the head, and head-tilting – changes that indicate the degree of boredom, or a less than equable frame of mind. If it spots any of these, the hand-held computer vibrates, alerting the user to change tack or draw the conversation to a close. The researchers trained the computer by showing it over a hundred eight-second video clips of actors displaying specific emotions. Now, when presented with previously unseen video clips, the system correctly predicts people's emotions 90 per cent of the time when analysing actors, and 64 per cent of the time when looking at shots of ordinary people. The researchers are now training their software with footage from movies and webcams, and working on a way to shrink the camera and computer to a comfortable size.

Probiotics for poultry: the way to a salmonella-free chicken

Every year in the UK at least ten million unfortunate victims end up locked to a loo seat for longer than they'd like thanks to something they ate, and poultry is a common culprit. That's because chickens and other birds often carry pathogenic bacteria which, if the meat is not carefully prepared, can infect the consumer. To combat the problem, researcher Billy Hargis is giving his chickens a dose of probiotic 'good bacteria' – similar to the yoghurts on sale in the health-food store – in a bid to cut the potential for food poisoning due to bugs like salmonella and campylobacter. The idea is that the good bacteria will compete for nutrients and resources, pushing out the harmful gut pathogens.

To isolate them in the first place, Hargis's team collect the natural bacterial flora from healthy chickens, confirm that the bugs they have isolated can compete effectively against the pathogen, grow them and then administer them to chicks in their feed and water. Also, adding prebiotics – substances that encourage the growth of the good bacteria – to the diet can help to maintain a thriving intestinal population. At the moment the researchers are currently working to achieve the perfect cocktail of good bacteria, but the fruits of their labours have already been embraced by a number of commercial poultry farmers eager to cut the levels of food-poisoning bacteria in their produce.

SPACE

The human centrifuge for exercise in space

Scientists at the University of California have come up with a novel way to prevent the muscles of astronauts from wasting away under micro-gravity conditions – with a 'space cycle'. Essentially a human-powered centrifuge, researcher Vincent Caiozzo's machine generates artificial gravity by turning in a circle, and carries two astronauts at a time. One pedals on a bike to drive the device, while the other stands on a platform performing squat-thrusts against the 'gravity' generated by his companion. The space cycle, which can be fitted with any kind of exercise equipment, provides the equivalent of an off-world multi-gym and means that, even in micro-gravity, astronauts can still do essential bone-loading exercises to keep their muscles and skeletons in shape.

Vibrate your way upright

Scientists from the USA have succeeded in helping unsteady patients to improve their sense of balance by installing vibrators in the soles of their shoes. Diabetics, the elderly and some stroke sufferers are prone to stumbling because nerves signalling the positions of joints and the contact of the feet with the floor can sometimes fail to transmit the messages faithfully. But by embedding small motors inside a series of silicone-gel insoles so that low-level, imperceptible vibrations could be applied to the heel and forefoot regions of wearers, Boston University researcher Jim Collins and his colleagues were able to make previously fall-prone patients much steadier on their feet. The researchers suggest that, by adding neurological 'noise' to the nerves in the feet, the vibrations may actually enhance the ability of the nervous system to pick up the pressure changes that accompany an altered posture and hence improve balance. The technique, the scientists point out, could be particularly helpful for the elderly, with falls accounting for a significant number of mortalities and injuring approximately one-third of over-sixty-fives annually.

Fancy attending a virtual funeral?

Wacky Australians have built a 120-seater crematorium complex, complete with state-of-the-art visual technology to help families record funeral services. It also boasts facilities to give musical, video or multimedia presentations, and will even broadcast the proceedings on the Internet so that relatives abroad can participate in a virtual funeral!

Does Pokémon cause cancer ...?

In the first example of its kind, a US cancer-research institute has been threatened with legal action by the makers of the Pokémon card game after one of its researchers borrowed the company's trademark to name a newly discovered gene. Naming the gene after the game would probably not normally have provoked much of a fuss, were it not for the fact that Pier Paolo Pandolfi, from the Memorial Sloan-Kettering Cancer Center in New York, had discovered a gene that causes cancer. As a result, news headlines along the lines of 'Pokémon Causes Cancer' sprang up around the world. Naturally, the company was concerned about the possible impact this may have on its image and threatened to sue if the malign gene was not renamed.

This is not the first time a scientist has been landed in hot water by naming a gene after a high-profile trade-marked product. In 1993, Cambridge researcher Alfonso Martinez Arias was told to rename his 'Velcro' fly gene after the Velcro Corporation claimed that he was diluting the value of their name and mark. So far, though, US researcher Bob Riddle, who named another gene Sonic Hedgehog in 1993, appears to have escaped notice.

The Sloan-Kettering scientists have now agreed to rebrand their Pokémon gene under the slightly less catchy title Zbtb7.

Can you really smash concrete with kung fu?

Members of the Institute of Physics in London have resorted to kung fu in recent years to punch home the message that science is cool. By smashing through eight-centimetre-thick blocks of concrete with their bare hands, the IOP scientists have been showing the public why physics is behind some of the world's biggest break-throughs. But what is the key to smashing a concrete block successfully? You have to supply the absolute maximum kinetic energy, so the strike with the heel of the hand has to be as fast as possible (since kinetic energy is proportional to speed squared); you must get your maximum weight behind it (because kinetic energy is also proportional to the mass); and you have to aim beyond the surface of the block to ensure maximum strike speed (otherwise the brain slows the hand down as it nears the concrete surface). And does it hurt? Well, I cannot tell a lie: yes it does. But not half as much as if you stop believing you can break it, and slow your hand down!

 FACTOID:

'Putting your ear to a railway track can tell you if a train is coming.'

TRUE

Unhappily, however, it cannot tell you which *direction* it is coming from – as a Romanian man found out when placing his ear against the rail to listen for the approach of his train. Demonstrating his technique to a crowd of supposedly impressed onlookers, he was run over by an express train coming the other way.

Will machines ever be able to replace human tea-tasters or wine-tasters?

Scientists in the Netherlands have built an artificial 'throat', to help speed up the process of testing and synthesising the flavours of drinks. Most of what we call 'taste' is actually down to our noses. Try holding your nose and then placing something strong-tasting in your mouth; you won't be able to taste it – and that's because when we eat or drink something the aromas contained in the food are released inside the mouth and then puffed up into the nose, where we 'smell' them. It's the combined sensations produced by both the tongue and the nose that give something its flavour, but drink flavours are very difficult to get right because liquid spends so little time in the mouth before being swallowed.

To solve the problem, Alexandra Boelrijk at NIZO Food Research, together with colleagues at the flavourings company Quest International, and Wageningen University in the Netherlands, set up two glass tubes, one placed vertically above the other, connected by a short piece of rubber tubing that could be closed with a clamp. The top tube was the 'mouth' while the bottom tube represented the oesophagus (gullet). At the bottom of the model they attached an air supply to blow gas up the tube at the same rate as a normal human exhalation. They added small amounts of flavoured liquid to the 'mouth', then opened the 'throat' (the clamped rubber tube) to simulate swallowing, and once the liquid had drained turned on the airstream to simulate exhalation. They tested the 'breath' collected from the top of the mouth and analysed it. The researchers found that, for all of the flavours they tested, the breath analysis from their model precisely matched the aroma profile produced when the same flavour was given to real people to drink. This means it should be possible to test complicated flavour mixtures in modern beverages much more quickly and cheaply, and without having to poison anyone's taste buds in the process.

Sorting out the nuts from the nots

A bag of pistachio nuts always contains a few unopened specimens, largely because the process used to sort the open from the closed nuts is far from perfect. But now a Kansas-based inventor, Tom Pearson, has come up with a sound way to separate the two – by creating a machine that can tell the difference between the noises made when opened and closed nuts clatter on to a steel tray. Compared with their open counterparts, unopened nuts make a shorter ringing sound when they drop, and these unwanted specimens are blown away with a puff of compressed air. Capable of sorting twenty-five nuts a second, the new machine is slower than the existing technique, which relies on opened nuts being caught by a series of needles as they are spun in a drum, but the new system is 97 per cent accurate, a significant improvement on the 90 per cent scored by the needle method. This 7 per cent could save companies up to half a million pounds a year, a lot of frustrated customers and more than a few broken teeth!

 FACTOID:

'In London there is a special memorial commemorating all the animals, birds and other creatures that ever made a formal contribution to British military efforts at war.'

TRUE

It is in Park Lane, and included in the sculpted representations are horses, mules, pigeons, dogs, camels, elephants, monkeys, canaries, and even the glow-worms that helped First World War soldiers read their maps in the trenches at night.

Country music can't make you kill yourself, can it?

The 2004 Ig Nobel Prize for Medicine – one of a series of awards intended to recognise research findings that 'make people laugh, and then think' – was awarded to two US doctors who have discovered an unusual cause of suicide: country music. Steven Stack from Wayne State University, Michigan, and James Gundlach of Auburn University, Alabama, found that cities in which radio stations play an above-average amount of country music have higher-than-average suicide rates. Statistically, however, black people appear to be immune to the effect.

Was it because he used fizzy soft drinks that a Roman farmer was an *agri-cola*?

Also in 2004, Pepsi and Coke saw sales shoot up nearly 1000 per cent in some agricultural areas of India. But the surge wasn't due to thirsty farmers. Instead, word had got round that spraying the drinks on crops was a cost-effective way to deal with insect pests! The farmers say that the sticky, sweet drinks attract ants, which protect the crop by eating the larvae of insect pests. Their claims are, however, being refuted by Indian researchers who have since carried out tests on sample crops and 'not seen any increase in productivity, or eradication of pests'. It is not clear, though, whether they tested diet varieties too, which should be sufficient to put off even the most determined pests.

Pepsi and Coke issued statements declaring that there is 'no scientific basis' for the practice, but given that a litre of pesticide costs about £100, and the same volume of Coke about 30p, the farmers felt it was well worth taking a gamble!

FORENSIC SCIENCE

Trapping illegal ivory traders

The worldwide ban on ivory trading was introduced in 1989 after elephant populations fell precipitously by 60 per cent from over 1.3 million in 1979 to around half a million by 1987. Despite the ban, however, conservationists estimate that four thousand elephants, hippos and other ivory-bearing animals are still being killed every year to fuel the trade which, according to the latest analysis of seizure data in the Elephant Trade Information System (ETIS), has been increasing in volume since 2004 and moved sharply upward in 2009. One culprit responsible for boosting the illegal ivory trade recently is the Internet, because individuals can buy and sell anonymously using facilities like eBay. But, at the same time, trades on the web like this are very hard to regulate because the word 'ivory' is commonly used – quite innocently – in other ways, such as in the expressions 'ivory soap' and 'ivory wedding dress'.

But now a team at the University of Washington has come up with a powerful new tool to help in the battle against illegal poaching of ivory. Samuel Wasser and his colleagues have constructed a genetic map of the elephants from sixteen nations in Africa, enabling them to pinpoint the origins of a piece of ivory, with 80 per cent accuracy, to within a radius of six hundred miles. They constructed the genetic database by isolating DNA from elephant dung and pieces of skin and then identified the genetic differences between elephant populations in different parts of Africa to produce their overall map. DNA extracted from a piece of ivory can now be used to pinpoint where it came from, helping to identify poaching hot-spots.

Do cells from a baby remain in the mother for ever?

Scientists have known for some time that cells often jump across the placenta from a developing baby to enter the mother's bloodstream, but until recently the ultimate fates of these cellular trespassers remained a mystery. Now, New England Medical Center scientist Diana Bianchi and her colleagues have discovered that, once they enter the mother's bloodstream, these foetal stem cells infiltrate a range of organs, where they transform themselves into specialised cells in the thyroid, intestine, cervix and gall bladder; they can even help to heal skin injuries. At the moment the team isn't clear what contribution, if any, these cells make to the healing process, but an attractive hypothesis is that these foetal stem cells are helping to repair injuries sustained by the mother, in what the researchers refer to as 'pay-back' for the price of pregnancy.

But it's worth noting that a number of autoimmune diseases – conditions in which the immune system turns upon the body's healthy tissues – are much more common in women who have given birth, compared with women who have never been pregnant. It is possible that these autoimmune diseases, which include diabetes and thyroid disease, could occur *because* the trespassing foetal cells fool the immune system into attacking tissues that it shouldn't.

ZOOLOGY

What do you do if you see an endangered animal eating an endangered plant?

That's what they're asking in Mount Eccles National Park in Victoria, southern Australia. Victoria is home to the largest number of wild koalas of all the states in Australia. The total koala population in Australia plummeted from around seven million at the time when Europeans first arrived in the late 1700s to as few as a hundred thousand now. The current growth of the koala population is, however, putting too much strain on the eucalyptus trees, which form their staple diet. The long-term preservation of the species depends upon the preservation of their habitat, so conservationists plan to put two thousand of the koalas on 'the pill' to slow down the population boom. According to Ian Walker, project manager, the method that has been chosen is a matchstick-sized hormone implant inserted under the skin between the shoulder blades. The implant, as used by women all over the world, releases small amounts of female hormones to prevent pregnancy and lasts about six years. The benefit of using this approach is that it is minimally invasive and completely reversible: full fertility is restored once it is removed.

FACTOID:

'The Eiffel Tower is fifteen centimetres taller in mid-summer than it is in mid-winter.'

TRUE

Due to the expansion of metal when it's warm, the Eiffel Tower grows and shrinks by that much each year.

MARINE ECOLOGY

Scientists seal a deal to monitor polar oceans

Rather than send ships to sea to gather research data, why not ask an animal to do it for you? That was the thinking behind a project headed by St Andrews University Sea Mammal Research Unit scientist Mike Fedak, who recruited a new breed of assistant – elephant seals – to help him to study remote polar waters. Traditionally, studies of the oceans, which can help in weather prediction and monitoring climate change, are made by towing probes behind ships in order to measure salinity, depth and water movements. But researchers tend to be limited to studying areas where ships are going already, so some regions, such as the Antarctic, are more difficult to access than others.

Fedak and his team solved the problem by producing a fist-sized probe and transmitter, which they attached to the heads of elephant seals. These animals dive forty times a day to depths ranging from three hundred to eight hundred metres to hunt for fish and squid. Equipping them with the probes meant the seals could make measurements of temperature, pressure and salinity many times per day in multiple locations. The information collected by the devices was automatically transmitted, whenever an animal surfaced, to a satellite, which in turn relayed the information, together with the position of the animal, on to the waiting oceanographers. The team initially tested the devices on two beluga whales off Norway before conducting a larger three-year trial which involved seventy elephant seals from four breeding areas around the Southern Ocean.

Food for thought: scientists uncover basis of popcorn popping potential

Researchers in Indiana have sussed out how science can solve the problem of unpopped corn, which is notorious for cracking teeth and dislodging fillings. By comparing the structure of good and bad 'popping' varieties, Purdue University scientist Bruce Hamaker and his colleagues were able to pin the problem down to the cellulose-rich outer shell of the corn, called the pericarp. The best popcorn comes from corn with the strongest peri-carp – which works like a pressure-cooker, keeping the corn locked up tight until it reaches bursting point and explodes. Hopefully, this new knowledge means that it should be possible to identify or even breed strains of corn with superior popping potential.

THE SENSES

Can smells boost alertness?

Yes, or so it would seem. According to a study carried out on stressed drivers, a whiff of peppermint or cinnamon odour boosted alertness, decreased levels of frustration and anxiety, and lessened fatigue. Professor Bryan Rauden-bush, a psychologist at Wheeling Jesuit University in West Virginia, took subjective measures of cognitive performance, wakefulness, mood and workload as volunteers took part in a stimulated driving task and were exposed at various times to different concentrations of the two odours, or normal air as a control. In general, prolonged driving led to increased anger and fatigue, and decreased vigour among the participants. But fatigue ratings were lower when the subjects were exposed to the cinnamon scent, and both cinnamon and peppermint produced increased ratings of alertness compared with the air control. According to Raudenbush, these agents serve as central-nervous-system stimulants. 'Periodic administration of these odours over long-term driving may prove beneficial in maintaining alertness and decreasing highway accidents and fatalities.' So maybe everyone should now invest in a dangly pepper-mint or cinnamon air freshener for the car?

MEDICINE

Brain injuries are time-consuming to diagnose – can anything up speed the process?

Researchers at Drexel University in Philadelphia have developed a hand-held monitoring device that can non-invasively pick up signs of bleeding into and around the brain, using just light. The hairbrush-sized clot-spotter uses a technique called functional near-infrared (fNIR) optical imaging and works by shining near-infrared light through the skull and underlying brain tissue. Collections of blood around the brain, or within the brain itself, cause the light to be absorbed differently compared with normal tissue, flagging the area as a 'hot-spot'. The information picked up by the probe is then transmitted wirelessly to a PDA or palmtop computer, which maps out the head and highlights potential problem areas.

In a pilot study involving 305 patients at Baylor College of Medicine in Houston, Texas, the device picked up 100 per cent of bleeds around the brain (known as subdural and epidural haematomas) and 98 per cent of bleeds into the brain, with no false positives. As a result it could make a significant contribution to the management of head-injured and stroke patients, whose care can sometimes be delayed while doctors carry out a CT scan of the brain to determine the best course of action.

Professor Kambiz Pourrezaei, one of the Drexel team, points out that it is also likely to solve the problem of finding head injuries in very young children brought to hospital following a fall. The device went on sale internationally in October 2008, marketed under the trade name Infrascan.

Fish help to pollinate flowers

In an elegant study, researchers in the USA have shown how fish really can contribute to the pollination of flowers, highlighting the complex interdependence between totally different species. University of Florida ecologist Robert Holt and his colleagues staked out four ponds, two with fish and two without, and counted the number of pollinating insects, including bees and butterflies; the diversity and quality of the surrounding plant life; the number of dragonflies around the ponds; and the number of dragonfly larvae in the ponds. The team found large numbers of dragonfly larvae and mature dragonflies around those ponds that had no fish. These ponds also had the poorest surrounding plant growth and the fewest pollinating insects. But the ponds full of fish were surrounded by plant life that was much better pollinated, and showed a greater number of pollinating insects and far fewer dragonflies and their larvae. It turns out that dragonflies eat pollinating insects, but fish eat dragonfly larvae – so that more fish means fewer dragonflies, more pollinating insects and happier plants. This study shows how human influences on one isolated aspect of an ecosystem – such as fishing – could have far-reaching consequences for many other animal and plant species.

FACTOID:

'At the top of a mountain, the proportion of oxygen in the air is lower.'

FALSE

Air pressure is much lower, and there is less oxygen overall, but the *proportion* of the air that is oxygen is exactly the same – about 20 per cent.

TECHNOLOGY

How did you know I was just about to go up to the bar to get another drink?

Thirsty researchers at the University of Munich, led by Andreas Butz, have developed a beer mat that automatically prompts bar staff for a refill when a glass is empty. The mat uses a pressure sensor to detect when the glass is getting low, and then signals the bar by radio for a top-up. The developers suggest that it could also be used as a bar-room voting device – for instance, in a karaoke setting, whereby drinkers quite literally raise their glasses to a good act. Unkind Germans, Australians and North Americans might alternatively suggest that for British beer drinkers an electric heating element could also be installed to ensure that the beer is suitably warm upon serving . . .

An electric answer to deafness?

Researchers at the National Physical Laboratory in Teddington have come up with a hearing aid that may help deaf people to appreciate music. Their device builds upon current cochlear-implant technology, which uses electrodes to stimulate the nerves in the cochlea – the part of the ear that converts sounds into nerve signals the brain can understand and that is damaged in some forms of deafness. Although current cochlear implants can help people to comprehend some aspects of speech, they only respond to certain sound frequencies, making music difficult to interpret. But the system being developed by Markys Cain and his colleagues consists of a series of tiny bar-shaped elements coated with a piezoelectric material called polyvinylidene fluoride. (Piezoelectricity is the electrical field or electric potential produced when some materials are subjected to mechanical strain.) By adjusting the length and shape of these elements the device can be 'tuned' to vibrate at a much wider range of sound frequencies. These vibrations deform the piezoelectric coating, generating tiny electrical currents, which can be relayed to the auditory nerve as with a standard cochlear implant. The researchers believe that ten to twenty of the resonating elements would be required to enable users to understand speech, and adding just a few more could provide sufficient resolution to appreciate music.

The prototype that the team is now working on, which contains over a hundred sensing elements, measures about two centimetres square, but the researchers are working on a miniature version capable of fitting inside the ear. Another major advantage of their approach is that, unlike the present system, which requires an external power supply, the piezoelectric device can be entirely self-contained. The only downside is that the team anticipates that it may be ten years before the device is produced commercially.

Scratch-free screens for phones and MP3 players?

Try as you might to look after your hand-held electronic gadgets, inevitably they end up fighting with keys and pens in pockets, meaning that the screens are eventually covered in unsightly scratches. But now there may be a solution, thanks to the invention of a highly scratch-resistant coating developed over the last few years by the Japanese media-manufacturing giant TDK. The new polymer coating is so tough that a CD protected by it remained blemish-free even after being assaulted with wire wool and an arsenal of marker pens. Only a very determined attack with a Swiss Army knife eventually succeeded in damaging the disc surface.

The coating is applied in two layers. The first layer consists of tiny (fifty-micrometre) particles of silica (glass) embedded in a fluorine-containing resin. The silica provides strength while the fluorine repels water, preventing inks or paints from sticking to the surface. The top layer consists of a curing agent, called aceto-phenone, and another fluorine-containing resin. The mixture is 'set' with a quick blast of ultraviolet light. The new material has been welcomed by rival media manu-facturers including Sony, Panasonic and Philips, and could easily be incorporated in the screens of the average mobile phone or MP3 player before too long.

PHOTOGRAPHY

Say cheese – oops, hit the button too late . . .

Have you ever waited ages for the perfect picture and then missed the moment because you were a fraction of a second too fast or too slow in hitting the button? If this sounds like you, then Kodak may have the solution, with an invention for their digital camera range called BLILO – short for 'burst last in last out'. Once the BLILO button is pressed, the camera continuously shoots pictures at the rate of two a second, storing them on a separate thirty-two-megabyte memory card. Once thirty pictures have been shot, the camera starts over-writing the old images with new ones, indefinitely. When the button is released, the last four frames taken – one of which hopefully contains the crucial moment – are transferred to the camera's main memory.

'Pedalling' a solution to cycle visibility

Richard Hicks, a UK-based inventor, has come up with an ingenious way to make cyclists even more visible on roads at night: pedals that incorporate tiny dynamos to drive ultra-bright LEDs embedded in the front, rear and sides of the bike's pedals. The system charges up a super-capacitor, which stores charge and makes sure that the lights keep shining – and the cyclist remains visible – for up to twelve minutes even when stopped at traffic lights and alongside other vehicles. The new power pedals are marketed as Pedalite KPL100 and are sold in pairs. You just unscrew your existing pedals and replace them with Pedalites.

Piezo – *E. coli* probe?

Raj Mutharasan, an engineer at Drexel University in Philadelphia, Pennsylvania, has developed a hand-held sensor that can pick up signs of food poisoning, such as *E. coli* contamination, in seconds. The device, which is as simple to use as a thermometer, employs the piezoelectric effect to weigh up how many microbes there are in a sample. It consists of a fine glass thread five millimetres long and one millimetre thick which is coated with a piezo-electric ceramic substance called lead zirconate titanate (PZT). This layer is also peppered with antibodies which recognise the harmful O157 strain of *E. coli*. When an alternating electric current is applied, it causes the PZT coating to expand and contract, making the glass thread vibrate at a certain frequency, which can be measured. But when the antibodies lock on to *E. coli*, the weight of the bacteria applies drag to the thread, slowing the rate of the vibrations; the more bacteria there are, the greater the change in the vibration frequency. The sensor works in liquid extracted from the food being examined, and tests so far show that it can detect as few as four bacterial cells in one millilitre of liquid. It can also pick up other pathogens, including listeria, and various agencies are now teaming up with the Drexel researchers to explore its potential in the detection of bio-terror weapons such as anthrax.

Snails that can fly?

In his famous book *On the Origin of Species*, Charles Darwin pointed out that there are many remote islands on Earth populated by snails that seem to be very similar to snails found elsewhere. Yet snails can't swim and their eggs are destroyed by seawater – so how did they get there? Darwin speculated that snails might be stowing away aboard migrating birds, but quite how, he was at a loss to say. Now, though, a team of researchers led by Cambridge geneticist Richard Preece has used the power of DNA technology to prove that Darwin was almost certainly right.

The researchers genetically fingerprinted a species of European *Balea* snails and compared them with similar snails found nine thousand kilometres away on the remote Tristan da Cunha Islands in the South Atlantic. The genetic sequences are almost identical. But the snails couldn't have travelled there by boat, since the islands were first populated only five hundred years ago and the snails' DNA 'clock' – a measure of the differences between their DNA and that of their European counterparts – suggests that they have been on the islands for much longer than that. Nor are similar snails found on any other nearby land-masses, so they couldn't have floated there. So, the researchers conclude, the only way these snails could have made their journey to these remote islands was by air – exactly as Darwin thought. In fact, these snails create a particularly sticky mucus, which enables them to glue themselves tightly to birds' feet and feathers. The Tristan da Cunha Islands are also a common destination for European migratory birds looking for a warm place to spend the winter, making the theory that much more plausible.

Dirt-repellent clothes that always stay clean? Now you're talking

Housewives (and house-husbands) may soon have emptier laundry baskets and lower water bills to look forward to, thanks to researchers at Clemson University in South Carolina who have discovered how to make fabrics dirt-resistant. They've developed a new highly water-repellent coating that is made from a polymer gel (polyglycidyl methacrylate) which is mixed with silver nano-particles. The result promises to offer superior resistance to dirt, meaning that it needs cleaning much less often. Treated clothes can be made in any colour because the coating is added after the material has been dyed.

Phil Brown, one of the researchers behind the new coating, likens the concept to a lotus plant, the leaves of which are known to 'self-clean' by repelling dirt and water. When water does come along, any dirt present is carried away much more easily. In the same way, dirt can simply be sprayed or wiped from clothes made with the new coating, which, unlike conventional water-repellent coatings, is permanently bonded to the fabric so it can't wash off.

The team is now working on a way to engineer anti-microbial particles into the coating, which would nullify body odours (so a wearer would presumably not need to wash either!) and could also help to neutralise other nasty niffs, including the smell of cigarette smoke.

 FACTOID:

'The acid in most car batteries is hydrochloric acid.'

FALSE

It is sulphuric acid.

Rats – and humans – that can smell in stereo

Scientists in India have found that in just one sniff (lasting about a tenth of a second), and despite having nostrils only three millimetres apart, rats can tell which direction a smell is coming from. The same, they say, is probably also true of humans.

Raghav Rajan and his colleagues at the University of Agricultural Science in Bangalore trained rats to lick one of two water spouts according to where they thought a piped-in smell was coming from. Incredibly, the rats were correct 80 per cent of the time, but when the researchers temporarily blocked one of their nostrils, the animals' performances dropped considerably. To find out how the rats were achieving this olfactory feat, the researchers next recorded the electrical activity in the parts of the brain responsible for processing smells. They found populations of nerve cells that responded selectively to the direction from which smells arrive. These cells essentially compare the smell signals coming into both nostrils; whichever cells switch on first then switch off their counterparts on the other side of the brain, enabling the animal to pinpoint the origin of a smell. And because the human olfactory system is wired up in a very similar way, it is likely that the same thing is true for us – so those TV adverts and comic strips showing kids following their noses to find a feast are science fact rather than science fiction.

The river's high . . . on cocaine

Researchers in Italy have published the world's first report tracking cocaine use in Italian cities – by analysing the local river water. Ettore Zuccato and colleagues from Milan's Mario Negri Institute for Pharmacological Research tested water samples from the River Po as well as water-treatment plants serving several medium-sized cities and found that at least $US400,000 worth of excreted cocaine was flowing along the river each day! The findings suggest that the existing estimates of cocaine use – roughly fifteen thousand doses daily – are significantly short of the mark, and that, realistically, more than double that number – forty thousand doses – are probably being consumed in the region every day.

So sex doesn't sell after all

According to a study run by psychologists at the University of Michigan and involving more than three hundred student volunteers, what you watch on the box can seriously damage your susceptibility to advertising. Researcher Brad Bushman asked male and female participants to watch a violent, sexually explicit or neutral television programme. The ads originally in the programmes had been replaced with violent, sexual or neutral ads for real products. The participants were asked, after watching the programme, to recall the brand names of the advertised products they'd seen. Brand recall, Bushman found, was 17 per cent higher for participants who had seen a neutral programme compared with a violent programme, and 21 per cent higher than for those who saw a sexually explicit programme. Violent adverts were also 20 per cent less memorable than the sexual ones, and 18 per cent less memorable than the neutral adverts. According to Bushman, 'People are less likely to remember brands advertised in violent and sexually explicit programs. Sex and violence just don't sell, in other words.' Which has obvious implications for sponsors and advertisers. But, mildly flirtatious intimations – *à la* 'Naked Scientists', for instance – appear to work just fine. At least in the author's experience!

Can we predict the weather four months ahead?

UK climate scientist Tim Palmer and his team at the European Centre for Medium-Range Weather Forecasts have found a way to predict rainfall, and hence the risk of certain disease outbreaks, four months into the future. Focusing on malaria, he's used an ensemble of climate models to come up with an early-warning system for where the disease is most likely to strike across parts of Africa.

The incidence of malaria is strongly linked to climate, with wetter years resulting in more widespread outbreaks of the disease. But by the time it is determined whether a year is 'wet' or 'dry', it has until now been too late to move resources to where they are most needed to treat sufferers, or to control the mosquitoes that spread the disease. The new weather-forecasting model, however, can predict the scale of the rainy season up to four months ahead of time, enabling infection-control teams and anti-malarial measures to be deployed in high-risk areas well in advance.

To come up with their new model, the researchers combined the forecasts of three different climate-predicting systems and then compared actual weather and malaria case records from the past twenty years with the model's predictions for the same period. Basing their work on specific regions of Botswana, they were able to show that the system made highly accurate retrospective predictions. In light of the five hundred million cases of malaria occurring worldwide each year, this finding potentially adds a powerful new weapon to our anti-malaria arsenal.

Injecting new life into a cold engine

Engineers at Colorado State University have come up with a clever way to make cars start more easily on cold days, and reduce the amount of unburnt particulate matter produced by a cold engine. In the new system, at start-up, a pump sucks out the volatile vapour hovering above the fuel in the tank and squirts it into the engine in place of the regular fuel. Being more volatile, this tank-top vapour burns much more readily, so the engine starts more easily and runs more cleanly. Once things warm up, the pump shuts down and the engine returns to getting its fuel in the normal way.

Why do wineglasses go foggy?

Researchers at Lehigh-Unilever have found out why some glasses develop a white discoloration with age and use that won't go away no matter how well you wash them. It's not down to dirty living but instead to tiny imperfections present in the glass when it was made. In a pristine new glass, most of the light that hits the glass surface passes through, with only a minimal amount being reflected back towards you. But with repeated cleaning, especially in a dishwasher, the inherent imperfections in the glass cause small cracks to open up in the surface. This has the effect of making light that shines on the glass ricochet off the surfaces of the cracks and reflect back towards the observer, making the surface look frosty. For exactly the same reason, snow looks white whereas water is transparent.

Is this *T. rex*'s relative?

Researchers in China have discovered the earliest known relative of *Tyrannosaurus rex*, filling in a big piece of the puzzle over where these 'tyrant dinosaurs' came from. Xing Xu of the Palaeontological Institute of Beijing together with colleagues internationally have described a pair of fossils dating back 160 million years that were uncovered in an area of north-west China in 2003. Tyrannosaur specimens found previously have all been roughly 65 million years old: although researchers were able to trace their history back 120 million years or so, previous considerable anatomical adaptations had obscured any evidence of their origins beyond that. But this new find – named *Guanlong wucaii* ('crowned dragon of the five-coloured rocks') – is a small (three-metre) beast which combines many of the features characteristic of its more 'modern' descendants, including U-shaped teeth and fused nasal bones, with many more primitive traits, including long arms, a three-fingered hand, blade-like teeth in the sides of the jaw and a primitive pelvis. Also, unlike the later tyrannosauroids, it had a small crest running from its snout to the back of its neck. This missing link means that researchers can write up more of where we now believe tyrannosaurs came from, and also designates them as close relatives of modern-day birds, which are descended from the same ancestor.

Useful tools for a vampire?

Anyone who gives blood or has had a blood test probably knows only too well that doctors can sometimes find it extremely hard – not to mention painful for the patient – to find a suitable vein. This is especially true of babies, on account of their small size; large people, among whom fat beneath the skin can cover up blood vessels; and individuals who are seriously dehydrated.

But help is now at hand in two separate developments. First, researchers at the Georgia Institute of Technology in Atlanta have developed a lightweight, portable ultrasound device to help doctors find blood vessels quickly, potentially saving precious minutes in an emergency. Their instrument – imaginatively named a 'vein finder' – consists of a disposable probe and needle guide linked to a box containing the electronics. The user slides the probe over the skin surface and an alarm is triggered when it locates a vein. A needle is then fed through the guide, which is positioned at just the right angle to ensure that the needle slides into the vein. The probe emits a thin beam of ultrasound about the width of a pencil lead, which is reflected by the tissue and back into the probe. Because blood moves around the body, the ultrasound frequencies reflected from a blood vessel are different from the frequencies bounced back from stationary tissue, enabling the device to pinpoint vessels with great accuracy. The frequencies also reveal the direction in which the blood is moving, allowing the device to distinguish between veins and arteries (because the blood they contain flows in opposite directions).

So far, the machine has proved highly effective in tests on laboratory tissue designed to model a human arm, and the team now plans to adapt it for human trials. The researchers point out that it could make a huge difference to obtaining rapid intravenous access not only in very young A&E patients (in whom veins are notoriously difficult to locate) but in those who have suffered trauma or cardiac arrest.

The second development comes via a researcher from the University of Pittsburgh, George Stetten. He has come up with another way for medical staff to pinpoint veins and other structures beneath the skin more easily: a sonic torch. Traditional ultrasound involves placing a probe on to the skin and then looking at an image on a computer screen next to the patient. This can make it difficult to relate what's on the screen to where something is located on the body. But the new system, dubbed a 'sonic flashlight', uses a probe equipped with a screen that projects what it is seeing on to a two-way mirror placed above the body part being examined. Looking through the mirror, the user then sees an image of what's beneath the skin apparently projected on to the skin surface. Medical students and nurses learning to insert intravenous cannulae were much more successful in their attempts to hit veins when they tested the system, and a clinical trial published in 2009 showed that, even in experienced hands, using the system could reduce the number of needle-prick attempts required to access a vein.

It's just the wine talking

Most people get chatty when they've had a few, but they may be competing with the wine itself in the future, if a recently launched Italian talking wine bottle design takes off. The brainchild of a Tuscan company called Modulgraf, the technology 'went live' in 2009 on bottles from the leading wine producer Allegrini, which is in the Valpolicella area of Italy. A special ink used on the bottle labels can be programmed with all the patter you would normally receive only from an experienced oenologist. To get at the stored information, would-be wine buyers thirsty for more details use a cigarette-packet-sized audio device to 'zap' the label and then listen as each bottle extols its virtues. Moreover, Modulgraf point out that, by virtue of the way it works, the system can also help to prevent counterfeiting, avoiding the problem of cheap imitations.

 FACTOID:

'A kettle full of hot (but not necessarily boiling) water weighs exactly the same as the same kettle containing the same amount of cold water.'

FALSE

Einstein's famous equation $E = mc^2$ stands for 'energy = mass [or weight] × the speed of light, squared'. Since the speed of light never changes, if the energy, or temperature, of the water in the kettle increases, then so must the weight, to keep the equation balanced.

Should you believe what people tell you?

US researchers from the Universities of Washington and California have found that they can fool people into avoiding certain foods by falsely telling them that they had a bad experience with the food as a child. Daniel Bernstein and his colleagues recruited a group of students and quizzed them about their dietary habits before returning some 'individual computer-generated feedback' to each of them. The 'feedback' – which was actually identical for all of them – said that they had been made ill by strawberry ice cream when they were little. When the group was later followed up and quizzed again, up to 40 per cent of them subsequently claimed that strawberry ice cream really had made them ill when they were very young, and that their inclination to eat strawberry ice cream had now distinctly lessened. Although the researchers were unable to achieve the same results with chips or chocolate ice cream, they suggest that their approach might help to prevent people, especially children, from eating unhealthily and carrying their bad eating habits into adulthood.

BACTERIA

Bacterial chemical camouflage

Scientists have worked out how we manage to carry around trillions of bacteria in our digestive tracts without causing our immune systems to go into meltdown. The bugs give themselves a sugary coating to disguise themselves as human gut cells. Using a common human intestinal 'good' bacterium, called *Bacteroides fragilis*, Harvard researcher Laurie Comstock and her colleagues found that the bacteria encourage intestinal cells to secrete a sugar called fucose, which the bugs then convert into a form called GDP-fucose and use to decorate the surfaces of their cells. Human cells do likewise, so it is tempting to speculate that the bacteria have evolved the technique as a form of chemical camouflage. More convincingly, when the researchers disabled a gene that enables the bacteria to add the sugar to their surfaces, mice carrying the modified bugs eliminated them within forty-eight hours. Unaltered bacteria, on the other hand, remained in the animals indefinitely.

ASTRONOMY

The first Martian shooting star

Analysing data sent back by the NASA Mars rover *Spirit*, researchers noticed a large streak across one of the images of the Martian sky. The timing of the photograph coincided closely (in March 2004) with the visit of a comet called Wiseman-Skiff and its attendant cloud of meteors. One of these meteors probably grazed past Mars at a leisurely eleven kilometres per second (seven miles per second), briefly lighting up the sky.

The images suggest that *Spirit* inadvertently captured astronomers' first glimpse of a shooting star as seen from Mars.

The findings are important because analysis of these events can provide information about the chemical events that take place when a meteor meets an atmosphere rich in carbon dioxide, just like that of the early Earth.

ZOOLOGY

Hummingbirds clock up an impressive feat of time-keeping

British and Canadian researchers have shown that hummingbirds have an impressive memory for times and places. Because they burn up calories so quickly, hummingbirds cannot afford to waste time and energy making repeat visits to flowers from which they have already collected nectar – at least, not until the flower has had time to replenish its sugar stores. As a result, these birds have evolved to memorise the locations of the flowers they have visited and exactly when; not only that, they can time their return journeys to within minutes of the flowers' replenishing their nectar supplies.

To show that this was the case, Edinburgh University's Susan Healy and her colleagues set up an array of eight fake flowers, each containing sugar solution, within the territories of free-living hummingbirds in the Canadian Rockies. Some of the flowers were refilled with sugar every ten minutes, whereas others were refilled every twenty minutes. The researchers monitored how often the birds visited each of the flowers. Incredibly, they appeared to be able to keep eight mental stopwatches running simultaneously, because they quickly learned to return to the ten-minute refill flowers after ten minutes, and the twenty-minute refill flowers after twenty minutes, and knew exactly which flowers they had visited at what time, and in what order! This was maintained throughout the course of a day. Although scientists were aware that hummingbirds had a good memory for places, no one had appreciated quite how good they are at keeping track of time too.

The wrong sort of music might be bad for you

Researchers from Italy and the University of Oxford have found that your choice in music can affect your stress levels. Peter Sleight and Luciano Bernadi played short excerpts from a range of musical genres, including

Beethoven, rap, techno, raga (Indian classical music) and Vivaldi, to twenty-four male and female volunteers, half of whom were musicians, half of whom were not. They found that the faster the music, and the more complex the rhythms, the greater the level of arousal among the subjects, which they assessed by recording heart rate and breathing. Conversely, more meditative, soothing tempos produce the opposite effect, with the raga inducing the greatest state of calm. Overall, the effects were most marked among the musicians – probably because they are trained to listen for a regular rhythm or beat in the music, with which they may then synchronise their breathing rate – but all of the subjects responded, leading the researchers to suggest that music therapy could be useful in the management of heart disease and strokes. The reverse implication is that people who listen all the time to fast music with complex rhythms may in fact be causing themselves unnecessary stress.

TECHNOLOGY

Helping people at night school see the light

A simple $15 solar-powered invention is making a world of difference to education in Africa. But because many people have to work for a living during the day, the only education accessible in many African countries takes place at night. And in remote villages without electricity, this can mean a class of forty crowding around a kerosene lamp, sometimes even having to take turns to see the words and pictures that can mean so much. As a result, teachers can struggle to convey key messages about nutrition and HIV awareness, and for many learners even basic literacy has been impossible to achieve. Now, though, the Kinkajou projector (named after the saucer-eyed South American mammal renowned for its prodigious night-time vision) looks set to change all that. This simple device was developed by the Design that Matters organisation working alongside students from Cambridge University and MIT, uses a superbright LED shone through plastic optics adapted from Fisher Price toys and a microfilm capable of holding ten thousand slide images. The slides are projected on to a screen or flat surface at a size suitable for class visibility. The LED bulbs last for a hundred thousand hours each and are far more robust than standard power-hungry incandescent projector lamps. They run from a twelve-volt solar-recharged battery. With one of these projectors a whole class can see and learn far more effectively.

FACTOID:

'All fish lay eggs.'

FALSE

All female fish produce eggs, but one or two species give birth to live young, notably the (female) Caribbean lemon shark and the (male) seahorse.

MEDICINE

Golden 'nanobullet' for cancer therapy

Researchers at the Georgia Institute of Technology have found that tiny filaments of gold (measured in nanometres, or millionths of a millimetre) can be used to home in on, and destroy, tumour cells buried deep in tissues. Mostafa and Ivan El-Sayed had shown previously that small spherical gold particles could be coated with antibodies to make them bind to a cell surface marker called an epidermal growth factor receptor (EGFR), which can occur in increased amounts on the surfaces of some cancer cells. These gold particles made it very easy to spot the cancer cells they had locked on to because they glowed when laser light of a certain frequency was shone on them. Unfortunately, visible light does not penetrate more than a few millimetres into tissue, and most cancers occur well beneath the surface, limiting the benefit of the gold method. But by stretching the nanospheres into a twenty-nanometre-by-sixty-nanometre rod, however, the researchers found that they would respond to laser light at longer, near-infrared wavelengths, which can pass harmlessly through healthy tissue to reach a tumour. This means that, within a cancer, the nanorods boost the absorption of the laser light, quite literally cooking the tumour cells. The El-Sayeds describe how an initial test using healthy and cancerous cells from the mouth showed that cancer cells coated with the gold nanorods could be destroyed using only half the dose of laser energy usually required to kill a cell.

PALAEONTOLOGY

There were reindeer in the Dordogne?

Reindeer could face severe stress at the hands of global warming, disappearing from large portions of their current ranges, scientists are predicting. According to Bordeaux University palaeontologist Françoise Delpech and University of Washington archaeologist Donald Grayson, who carried out a study of ancient reindeer bones unearthed in a cave in the Dordogne region that was also once home to Neanderthal man, reindeer are highly temperature-sensitive.

The research duo followed an archaeological sequence in the cave (meaning that the deeper you go, the older things are), dating from twelve thousand to over sixty-five thousand years ago. Based on the number of bones they unearthed from different time zones, they were able to compare reindeer populations with the summertime climate data for the region, which is known from pollen records dating from the same time periods. As summertime temperatures went up, they found, the number of reindeer went down, and when things really warmed up, about ten thousand years ago, the reindeer disappeared from the area altogether. 'Reindeer just cannot tolerate high summer temperatures,' Grayson says. 'They have almost no sweat glands, and keep their insulation – a heavy pelt – in summer.' So, if things really do heat up, it looks as if Santa could well be searching for a replacement for Rudolph in a hundred years or so. Let's hope he goes for an environmentally friendly alternative.

GM plants that come complete with their own carnivorous bodyguards

Dutch scientists have produced a genetically modified plant that calls up an army of carnivorous mites to attack pests that try to eat it. Wageningen University researcher Iris Kappers and her colleagues inserted a gene from a strawberry into a common experimental plant species called *Arabidopsis*. The resulting GM plants produced in their cells two new bodyguard-marshalling compounds called terpenoids. These chemicals are released whenever the plant tissues are damaged by pests and are strongly attractive to a species of predatory mites called *Phytoseiulus persimilis*, which swarm in from the surroundings to attack the hungry herbivore that mistakenly took a bite out of the wrong plant. A similar technique, the researchers say, could be used to protect common field crops, meaning that farmers would be less dependent on potentially toxic insecticide sprays.

Halt climate change by going veggie

UK-based physics consultant Alan Calverd has calculated that, methane emissions aside, rearing the animals we eat accounts for over 20 per cent of the anthropogenic (man-made) carbon dioxide released into the atmosphere each year. Given that the average meat eater consumes roughly their own body weight per year in meat, and that the rearing cycle for farm animals is at least three years, there's about three times the human population's weight of 'meat' on the planet at any one time. And, he argues, since we know how much carbon dioxide each kilogram of living tissue releases, we can work out that livestock-rearing accounts for a prodigious amount of carbon dioxide – in the region of seven billion tonnes, or a fifth of the total attributable to human activities – released into the atmosphere every year. Leaving meat off the dinner plate, even occasionally, suggests Calverd, could therefore help to slash greenhouse emissions and might even make the world's population healthier. So Paul McCartney's 'Meat-free Monday' could be a hit, though not necessarily a musical one . . .

Does marijuana damage your brain?

Despite marijuana's image as a relatively safe drug, and its decriminalised status in many countries, scientists have announced that it can produce long-term changes in the brain's blood-flow, and that the changes can still be present even after a month of not smoking. Ronald Herning and Jean Luc Cadet from the National Institute on Drug Abuse in Baltimore used non-invasive ultrasound tests to measure the flow of blood through the brains of fifty-four marijuana users and eighteen non-using controls. The researchers found that blood flowed much more quickly through the brains of the marijuana smokers, and that their vessels had a greater overall resistance to blood-flow compared with non-users. The changes were similar to (but greater than) those often seen in the brains of the elderly or of patients with chronic high blood pressure or long-term diabetes, suggesting that they are caused by the narrowing of small blood vessels.

But are the changes permanent? The researchers found that light to moderate marijuana users did show an improvement in their brain blood-flow after a month of abstinence, but among previously heavy users (more than seventy joints per week) the changes were irreversible, indicating that marijuana use may cause permanent abnormalities in the small blood vessels of the brain.

Mirror, O mirror, I ask you in rhyme What will I look like in five years' time?

A system under development in France supposedly makes it possible to predict how you will look in five years' time, based upon your present lifestyle. To begin, the computer takes a picture of you. It then builds up a profile of your behaviour by watching you at home, using a network of webcams which pick up couch-potato tendencies, including clandestine trips to the fridge for junk food or beer. The system also periodically enquires what you are eating or drinking. Once your profile is complete, the computer then calculates how this lifestyle will reflect on your appearance over five, ten or fifteen years. Too many snacks? It will add an extra chin or two. Too much alcohol? Prepare for wrinkles, a red nose and blotchy skin.

Marketing the system under the compelling name Persuasive Mirror, Accenture Technology intend to go on to produce a real-time system capable of providing users with a genuine sense of looking into the future to see how their present lifestyle is going to affect them, which, they say, might help motivate over-indulgers to make some changes before it's too late.

 FACTOID:

'The world's biggest slug can weigh up to fifteen kilograms (over two stones).'

TRUE

The Californian sea hare is a slug-like mollusc that lives underwater in kelp forests. It can grow up to a metre long.

MEDICINE

Cancers can't spread on their own: they need help

Scientists at the Sloan-Kettering Cancer Center in New York have added an important piece to the jigsaw puzzle of how cancers spread to other parts of the body – a process known as metastasis. Indeed, it is the spread to remote sites, rather than the original (primary) tumour itself, that causes the majority of cancer deaths, so tracking down how this process occurs is an important landmark in the search for effective anti-cancer therapies.

For many years researchers thought that cells merely peeled away from a cancer and travelled via the bloodstream to other tissues, where they seeded fresh tumours. But it turns out that that is not the whole story. Instead, cancers send an emissary first, in the form of bone-marrow cells. Researcher Rosandra Kaplan and her colleagues used mice that had been engineered to produce glowing green bone-marrow cells. When tumour cells (engineered to glow red) were injected into the mice the researchers first saw green (bone-marrow) cells appear in the animals' lungs and only after this had happened did the red tumour cells take up residence, in the same place, some time later.

Likening the process to preparing the nursery ahead of the arrival of a baby, the researchers think that cancers pump out signals that somehow mobilise bone-marrow cells and enable them to 'dock' in target tissues that the cancer will subsequently invade. Once the marrow cells have prepared the ground at the new site, tumour cells can move in. The team have now identified a cell marker rather like a molecular grappling hook that the tumour cells use to cling on to the bone-marrow cells. When this cellular marker was blocked chemically, no tumour spread occurred, suggesting that the same trick might work in humans with early-stage (pre-metastatic) cancers.

Novel diet tip: sleep in to lose weight

Scientists from the University of Bristol have found that obesity might be linked to not getting enough sleep. Dr Shahrad Taheri and colleagues measured the levels of two key appetite-regulating hormones, leptin and ghrelin, in blood samples collected from a thousand normal volunteers. Leptin makes people feel full, whereas ghrelin makes people feel hungry. The researchers found that subjects who reported habitually sleeping for only five hours a night had 15 per cent more appetite-boosting ghrelin and 15 per cent lower levels of appetite-suppressing leptin compared with people who slept for eight hours. The researchers argue that these appetite-stimulating hormonal changes probably make poor sleepers more likely to indulge in 'midnight feasts' and other food foraging behaviours that ultimately lead to overeating and weight gain. Indeed, the light sleepers in the study were statistically likely to be heavier. Over the last fifty years, the average person has reduced the amount of sleep that he or she gets per night by about two hours, which might be contributing to the present obesity epidemic. Good sleep, together with other lifestyle measures, may be an important way to reverse the present trend. So stay in bed for an extra hour or two and argue that it's part of your weight-control programme!

What mood was the Mona Lisa in?

According to research from the University of Amsterdam, the Mona Lisa is 83 per cent happy, 9 per cent disgusted, 6 per cent fearful and 2 per cent angry. That's the interpretation of Nicu Sebe's emotion-recognition software, which he is developing in collaboration with US scientists at the University of Illinois. Their algorithm examines key facial features, including the curvature of the lips and wrinkles around the eyes, to assign a score under six different emotional categories. Sebe used a database of 'neutral' young female faces against which to compare the expression of the Mona Lisa. Ultimately, the researchers are aiming to develop emotion-recognition systems to enable computers to recognise human moods.

A car paint that auto-repairs knocks and scrapes

Japanese car giant Nissan has developed the perfect product for careless drivers – a paint that automatically repairs minor scrapes and scratches. Called Scratch

Shield, the new coating comprises a highly elastic resin that forms a protective layer over the paint. If the bodywork is dented, but no paint is removed, heat from the sun melts the resin, which flows back into shape, returning the surface to its original smoothness and, in the words of Nissan's website, 'helping a vehicle maintain its new look for a longer period of time'.

MEDICINE

Salty water is a breath of fresh air for cystic fibrosis sufferers

Researchers in Australia and the USA have stumbled upon an extremely cheap yet highly effective way to help sufferers of the lung condition cystic fibrosis to breathe more easily – a dose of salt water. Scientists at the Universities of North Carolina and Sydney compared the lung function of almost two hundred cystic fibrosis patients given either a nebulised saline solution twice as salty as the sea to breathe in, or a placebo solution. They found that the patients given the strong salt solution showed significant improvements in lung function and day-to-day quality of life.

The effect seems to occur because the strong salt solution pulls water from the airway tissue on to the airway surfaces, making it much easier to shift the sticky mucus that accumulates in the lungs of cystic fibrosis sufferers. The University of North Carolina's Scott Donaldson, one of the doctors behind the study, said, 'We're very excited that this simple and inexpensive therapy turned out to be so effective and well-tolerated in patients with cystic fibrosis. It gives us great hope that the use of this therapy will reduce how often patients feel ill, will slow the decline of lung function, and will help these people live longer.'

What do you mean, 'this meat is off'? Off what?

Off the back of an unmarked van in a sidestreet, possibly. Researchers based at the University of Manchester have developed a technology that can identify contaminated meat in seconds, just by shining a light on it. At the moment, by the time a dodgy batch of meat is detected it could already be on the supermarket shelves or, worse still, in the stomachs of the unaware. But unlike existing techniques, which look for the bugs themselves, the new approach developed by microbiologist David Ellis uses infrared light to pick up the biochemical signatures of bacterial activity. As the number of bugs rises, so does the amount of waste they produce – and that is what the infrared beam can detect. So far the technique has been shown to work effectively for chicken and beef, but there is no reason it shouldn't work for other foodstuffs too.

The shortest distance between two points

A Florida-based inventor has come up with an idea for a 'stiff rope' to get round the problem of trying to hold out a line to someone from a boat or when climbing a rock-face. David Chroman's rope has a hollow plastic tube embedded down the middle of the strand. Blowing air into the tube from a compressed-air supply causes the rope to stiffen and become sufficiently rigid to support itself when held out from a boat, making it easily 'grabbable'.

What do your fingers say about your mood?

Canadian psychologists from the University of Alberta have found that the length of a man's index finger relative to his ring finger can be used to predict how inclined he is to be physically aggressive. Dr Peter Hurd and his team surveyed three hundred undergraduates and found that the shorter the index finger compared with the fourth finger, the more physically (but apparently not verbally) aggressive the individual tends to be throughout life. The relative lengths of the fingers depend upon how much testosterone the developing baby is exposed to in the womb: higher testosterone exposure produces a longer ring finger, and a more aggressive male. On the other hand – er, sorry about that – men with less 'masculine' finger lengths seem to be more prone to depression. But neither of these findings applies to women.

The results of the survey fit with other studies, including those of Dr John Manning, who measured the finger lengths of over three hundred footballers and found that those with the longer fingers tended to be superior in their abilities. The same applies to other sports, including judo, squash, track athletics and rugby. The Alberta team is now looking at the lengths of ice-hockey players' fingers to find out whether longer fingers are associated with more aggressive play (and hence more penalties).

PLANT BIOLOGY

Are *Acers* so called because they have an ace up their leaves?

Why do trees turn a pretty colour in autumn? Usually, it's due to the breakdown of chlorophyll, the green pigment that helps plants to turn sunlight into chemical energy. As the chlorophyll disappears, other vibrant colours within the leaf – including red- and golden-coloured molecules called carotenoids – are revealed.

But for some trees, including maples (the *Acer* species), the colour change might signal more sinister intentions. In these plants the leaves turn a beautiful scarlet colour because an additional class of molecules, called anthocyanins, are actively manufactured within the leaf just before it is dropped from the tree. Trees cannot afford to waste energy on a process that is not beneficial to them, so the colour change must serve some useful purpose. To find out what it might be, researchers Frank Frey and Maggie Eldridge from Colgate University in New York State prepared leaf extracts from maples and added them to some lettuce seedlings. The lettuce plants all promptly died, leading the researchers to suggest that, when maple trees drop their leaves, the anthocyanins leach into the soil, poisoning any other plants that might threaten to compete with the maple's own seedlings the following spring. The theory seems plausible because anthocyanins are chemically very similar to a substance called catechin, which is known to poison plant roots.

Where does the Ebola virus hide?

Scientists in Africa have solved a thirty-year puzzle surrounding the origins of the lethal Ebola virus – including where it comes from, and where it goes when it is not causing outbreaks among humans and primates. To track down Ebola's 'natural' host, Eric Leroy and his colleagues at the Centre International de Recherche Médicale de Franceville, Gabon, set traps to catch all of the small animals that they could close to sites of Ebola outbreaks. In all they collected over a thousand specimens, which they then analysed for signs of the virus. The tests showed that three species of fruit bat were positive. The researchers suspect that the virus could be finding its way into humans when hungry locals capture and eat infected bats, so they are now urging people to avoid the practice.

A hippo-thetical friendship?

Game wardens in Kenya rescued Owen, a one-year-old baby hippo, after they found him suffering from dehydration and separated from his herd. They temporarily put him into an enclosure in Haller Park with a 120-year-old giant tortoise called Mzee (Swahili for 'old man') and, says Sabine Baer, one of the senior park employees, 'he immediately lumbered over to the tortoise, which has a dark grey colour similar to grown hippos'. The two struck up an unlikely friendship and were almost inseparable. That is until Cleo, a female hippo Owen's own age, appeared on the scene more recently. Owing to Cleo's poor past record of treatment towards tortoises, Mzee was moved to safer surroundings. Keepers are hoping that Owen and Cleo will oblige with some offspring of their own.

PSYCHOLOGY

Why are there some songs you just can't get out of your head?

Frustrating, isn't it, having a tune go round your head that you just can't seem to shake off? Now British- and American-based scientists have pinpointed the part of the brain responsible for these 'earworm' effects, as they're known, by scanning the brains of volunteers who were experiencing them. The researchers played the subjects excerpts of well-known songs with short (two-to-five-second) silent gaps in them. As a control, they also played them songs they had never heard before, also containing gaps. The volunteers reported that in the well-known songs, even though the music had stopped, they could still 'hear' the song continuing inside their heads. So the areas of the brain that lit up on the brain scanner at these times must have been the ones responsible for filling in the gaps.

The researchers found that a region of the brain's temporal lobe called the auditory association area, which is located above the ear and is essentially where sounds are decoded and linked to meaningful information, became much more active during silent gaps in well-known songs. There was also a difference between songs that were instrumentals and those that contained lyrics: the instrumentals required a much greater amount of grey matter to reconstruct, presumably because the lyrics provide a short-cut for the retrieval of the information.

GEOLOGY

How can you escape from quicksand?

What is quicksand, how does it work, and are you likely to sink into it without trace? Moreover, what is the best way to escape if you do find yourself stuck in it? These were the questions bothering Dutch researcher Daniel

Bonn in 2005 when he wandered around some Iranian quicksand pits which, local legend has it, have been known to swallow camels from time to time, and for that matter anyone who cared to disagree with the local regime. To solve the riddle he collected some samples and, having analysed the mixture, recreated some Iranian quicksand in his lab to figure out how it works. There are four key ingredients, he found – sand (obviously), water, clay and salt. Together these materials form a structure resembling a house of cards, with large water-filled gaps between the sand particles, which are loosely glued in place by the clay. As long as it's left alone, the structure remains stable. But as soon as it's disturbed, the clay changes from a jelly-like consistency to a runny liquid. The effect is the same as stirring a pot of yoghurt. Liquefying the clay makes the quicksand about one million times runnier, and the whole house of cards comes tumbling down, with you inside it.

But he also discovered, to his surprise, that it is actually impossible to drown in it (as long as you don't do something stupid) – indeed, you should sink only to waist depth, because the density of quicksand is twice the density of a human body. But do not try to pull a stuck person out, he says, because the force required to extricate just a stuck foot is similar to that needed to move a medium-sized car, so you might inadvertently pull the person apart. The best way to escape is to turn a stuck body part in small circles to re-suspend the sand particles in water, withdrawing gently and gradually as you do so. Try to float, in fact, but be careful not to be too energetic about it!

Do women really rate wallet size over looks?

A study carried out by researchers at the University of St Andrews has shown that what women look for in a man has changed dramatically in recent years. Fhionna Moore and her colleagues surveyed 1851 women between the ages of eighteen and thirty-five and found that whereas in the past women had been attracted largely by the size of men's wallets and their consequent capability of maintaining their wives through their childbearing years, the woman of today values looks over riches. That said, younger, more ambitious, cash-strapped females in the study still rated a man's means over his looks – provided he was young, too.

Commenting on the study, Moore points out that economic constraints on women are not as strong as they were fifty years ago. 'It is this change, in comparison to historical constraints, that I believe influences mate preferences.' So it looks as if metrosexual man – complete with moisturiser – is here to stay.

FACTOID:

'All mammals are warm-blooded: it's one reason they are mammals, not reptiles.'

FALSE

The naked mole-rat is nature's only example of a genuinely cold-blooded mammal, but various others (like the hyrax or *dassie* of South Africa) rely on some time in full sunlight every day to be fully active.

PSYCHOLOGY

Is there a brain region that makes someone a trainspotter?

Some people take hoarding to extremes – and for some of them, yes, there would seem to be a compulsive element, although few studies have been carried out to investigate the phenomenon of compulsive collecting. But now scientists have pinpointed a part of the brain that appears to make people, and animals, want to collect things. Over seventy different animal species, including humans, show hoarding behaviour – which mostly involves stashing away food – but until a couple of years ago no one knew where in the brain the drive to collect (whether stamps, pencils, *Dr Who* videos or even loco-motive numbers) was based.

University of Iowa brain researchers Roy and Lucille Carver cracked the problem by studying the brain scans of a number of human patients who had developed unusual hoarding tendencies – to the extent that they would fill their houses with useless rubbish such as broken fridges, toasters or even junk mail. Although the items were useless to the patients, who otherwise showed normal brain function in terms of intellect and memory, the hoarders strongly resisted any notion of getting rid of the stuff. The researchers found that the patients with this hoarding behaviour all had small areas of damage to a particular part of the right side of the brain known as the mesial prefrontal cortex.

Now that they have pinpointed the region of the brain which drives collecting behaviour, scientists hope that this will provide clues to tackling the problem when it crops up in other conditions, including Tourette's, obsessive compulsive disorder, certain dementias and schizophrenia.

Who *needs* an excuse to have a glass of red wine?

Scientists have found that resveratrol – a well-known antioxidant in red wine – as well as helping to prevent arterial disease, can limit the progress of another condition known as cardiac fibrosis. When the heart is overworked by high blood pressure or heart failure, cells in the organ known as fibroblasts go into overdrive and produce an excessive amount of the fibrous tissue collagen. The accumulation of collagen makes the cardiac muscle much stiffer, to the extent that it eventually cannot pump efficiently. But Erik Olson and his colleagues at the Northeastern Ohio Universities College of Medicine have found that resveratrol can block the action of a key hormone known as angiotensin II, which is responsible for causing the production of excess collagen in the heart in the first place.

Using cells taken from the hearts of rats, the scientists found that pre-treating the cultured cells with resveratrol before adding the angiotensin II hormone prevented the fibroblasts in the culture from making excessive collagen, suggesting that the chemical might have anti-fibrotic properties when taken in moderation. Studies have shown that most dark (red) wines contain resveratrol – one of the vine plant's natural defences against disease – although amounts do vary between different varieties of grape, and the resveratrol content of any wine chiefly depends on the length of time the grape skins are present during the fermentation process. Some red wines therefore contain more resveratrol than others, so it may be better (and probably more enjoyable) to try them all. But before you do, be warned: doctors suggest that the greatest benefit to health comes from just one or two small glasses a day.

COMMUNICATIONS

No, boss, I'm ill at home. Whatever it sounds like, I'm in bed, honest ...

Imagine you're in a crowded pub, or out with someone you ought not to be, and your boss calls you on your mobile phone. The noise in the background would instantly betray your true whereabouts, and make it difficult for the caller to hear what you were saying over the din. But that could all be about to change if phone manufacturers adopt a phone design first put forward in 2004 by American inventor Jaime Siegel of Woodcliff Hill, New Jersey. The gadget uses two microphones – one placed on the side of the phone closer to your face, and the other on the opposite side, facing the noisy room or street. The mike closer to your face picks up what you say, plus the background noise, while the mike facing the room picks up mostly background noise. Now subtract one signal from the other . . . and you eliminate a lot of the background noise.

FACTOID:

'When people kiss, they both tilt their heads either to the left or to the right – it just depends on how they are positioned and how comfortable they are.'

FALSE

Most people not only get into the habit of tilting to only one side when they kiss a partner but may have a distinct preference for tilting that way in the first place. According to German researchers who secretly spied on kissing couples at railway stations, airports, beaches and parks, people are twice as likely to tilt their heads *right* as opposed to left.

Ivory trading's illegal, isn't it? Not if it's from a mammoth ...

Ivory trading is now almost entirely illegal, but there is one source of ivory that is perfectly within the law: the tusks of extinct mammoths. Mammoth ivory is of poorer quality than the elephant equivalent – it's very brittle and breaks easily, and also tends to smell – but business in it is booming. Between 1994 and 2001, seventy tonnes of mammoth ivory were shipped into Hong Kong, for distribution just within China. And Russia has been exploiting mammoth ivory for over two hundred years.

What could be more attractive than swallowing a magnet?

In late 2004 American radiologists felt the need to warn parents of the dangers of ingesting more than one magnet at a time! Although swallowing foreign objects is common among children, luckily 80 per cent of the swallowed objects pass harmlessly through the gastrointestinal system on their own, single magnets included. But consuming more than one magnet at once can spell disaster – because the magnets are attracted to each other across the walls of the intestines, with the result that loops of bowel become locked together. The ensuing life-threatening tangle can lead to tissue death and/or perforation of the intestinal wall. Not an attractive prospect . . .

Do whales get the bends?

Scientists have discovered that sonar from ships and submarines might be causing sperm whales to get the bends. Whales were thought to be immune to this condition, more formally known as decompression sickness or caisson disease, but Michael Moore and Greg Early from the Woods Hole Oceanographic Institution in the United States have found evidence of bone damage caused by the bends in the skeletons of a number of sperm whales, some from as long ago as the beginning of the twentieth century.

The damage to the whales' bones is thought to be the result of surfacing too quickly, which, just as in human scuba divers, causes tiny nitrogen bubbles to form in the blood, blocking small blood vessels and damaging the tissues they supply. The scientists think that whales, which often hunt for hours at a time at depths of getting on for two kilometres underwater, normally control their surfacing behaviour very carefully to avoid developing the bends. But if they are disturbed by underwater noises like sonar, explosions from sea-floor-mapping, or even earthquakes, they may surface too quickly, and develop the condition.

It's not just whales that are the victims, either. Recently, large numbers of dead giant squid have been washing up on beaches in South America with damaged ears, which is thought to be the result of exposure to underwater explosions detonated by companies surveying the sea floor for oil reserves.

FOOD

Curry wards off Alzheimer's

Researchers in California have found that turmeric, the yellow spice added to curry and some rice dishes, can block the formation of beta-amyloid, the abnormal protein that accumulates in the brains of patients with Alzheimer's disease. Turmeric, which is also known to have antioxidant and anti-inflammatory effects, has been linked previously to a reduced risk of Alzheimer's, and India, where it is a dietary staple, has the world's lowest rates of the disease. In the present study, University of California, Los Angeles, scientist Gregory Cole and his colleagues used mice genetically engineered to develop the rodent equivalent of Alzheimer's disease. They found that the small molecular size of the yellow pigment in turmeric, a substance called curcumin, allows it to penetrate brain tissues, mop up beta-amyloid, and break apart existing amyloid deposits with greater efficiency than many other drugs being tested as Alzheimer's treatments. A trial is currently under way at UCLA to establish what daily dose (one Madras or two?) would be required to lower Alzheimer's risk in humans. Scientists are also interested in the potential of turmeric's antioxidant and anti-inflammatory properties preventing other conditions, such as heart disease and cancer.

HUMAN BIOLOGY

Laugh all the way to the bank ... and save money on a gym subscription

Researchers at the University of Maryland School of Medicine have confirmed what the editors at *Reader's Digest* have claimed for years – that 'laughter really is the best medicine'. Michael Miller and his colleagues compared the responses of the blood vessels of twenty healthy volunteers when they were shown a funny film and when they were shown a mentally stressful film. The researchers used ultrasound to look at the function of the blood-vessel lining, called the endothelium, that plays a major role in regulating how relaxed, or open, blood vessels are. Damage to the endothelium is also linked to arterial disease. When the volunteers were shown the funny film, nineteen out of the twenty showed beneficial relaxation of the blood vessels and their blood-flow increased by 22 per cent. But when they watched the mentally stressful film, fourteen of the twenty study subjects showed a reduction in blood-flow by an average of 35 per cent, and changes in their blood-vessel reactivity persisted for up to forty-five minutes afterwards. The changes the team saw with laughter were at least as great as those measured when people exercise.

The research does not, however, reveal why the endothelium works less well to keep blood vessels open during mental stress, or why laughter is beneficial, but Miller suggests that it might be because stress in some way inhibits the production of the blood-vessel relaxant nitric oxide, which is secreted by the endothelium. The results of the study also agree with previous work published by the group in 2000, which showed that people with heart disease tended to respond with less humour to everyday situations than healthy individuals of the same age.

Sending songs into space

Sharing the arts with aliens appears to have been all the rage in recent years. On 4 February 2008 NASA beamed the Beatles' hit 'Across the Universe' into deep space to commemorate the song's fortieth anniversary, NASA's fiftieth birthday and fifty years since the launch of Explorer 1, the first US satellite. The transmission was aimed at the North Star, Polaris, 431 light-years away from Earth. Paul McCartney, who co-wrote the song with John Lennon, congratulated NASA and added, 'Send my love to the aliens. All the best, Paul.'

Perhaps NASA got the idea from a 2004 team of Swedish poets, who decided that citizens of other galaxies are in need of cultural enrichment and beamed samples of their work into space in the direction of Vega, the brightest star in the constellation Lyra. Unfortunately, because Vega is about twenty-six and a half light-years away, the poets will have to wait at least fifty-three years for any alien reviews to be forthcoming.

What's really in mineral water?

Bottled water is often considered to be purer than tap water – indeed, some hospitals give it to their patients in the belief that it is safer for them. But when Dr Rocus Klont and a team from the University of Nijmegen in the Netherlands studied sixty-eight commercially available mineral waters from nine European and seven non-European sources, they found that almost half – 40 per cent of the samples – were contaminated with bacteria or fungi. Bacteria from twenty-one of the samples could actually be grown in the lab. Klont points out that whereas the contaminants in the water may pose only a limited threat to healthy people, in people with increased susceptibility to infection – such as patients with HIV or those on immunosuppressive drugs – the risks may be much greater.

Solar cells that work on a cloudy day

Scientists from the University of Toronto have invented a flexible solar-cell material that is up to five times more efficient than current methods of turning the sun's energy into electricity. Unlike existing solar-cell technology, which uses visible light and is capable of turning up to 15 per cent of the light that hits the cell into usable electrical energy, the new 'plastic' material engineered by Ted Sargent and his team harnesses infrared light and can capture 30 per cent of the sun's power to produce electricity. And because it works on infrared, the new cell can produce electricity even on a cloudy day or in the dark, since, although visible light may be lacking, things that are warm – including people and animals – emit infrared radiation which the cell can use.

An added bonus is that the new material is also highly flexible, so it can be turned into a film to coat the surfaces of cloth, paper or other materials, potentially paving the way for wearable solar garments, which Sargent terms 'portable electricity'. Sargent is intending to commercialise the invention which, he says, could be on the market within five to ten years.

PLANT BIOLOGY

Can plants talk to each other?

They certainly seem to. Methyl jasminate (a constituent of the famous fragrance Chanel No. 5) is produced as a danger signal by a sagebrush shrub when it is attacked

119

by herbivores. Sagebrush shrubs nearby respond to this chemical alert by increasing the levels of their toxic defences, but other plants in the vicinity take note of the signal, too.

 FACTOID:

'The atmosphere is coldest over the North Pole.'

FALSE

It's coldest eighty kilometres above the equator. The *warmest* atmospheric temperatures are found three hundred kilometres above the poles, due to convection currents.

Ecologist Andrew Kessler from Cornell University in New York State has found that tobacco plants cultivated next to sagebrush plants begin to grow much more quickly when the sagebrush is clipped (to make it emit methyl jasminate) compared with when the plants are left intact. It seems that the chemical danger signal primes the tobacco to assume that it is itself about to be eaten, so it revs up its growth. This in turn leads to a boost in the levels of the precursors used by the tobacco plant to produce toxins, including nicotine. But to save resources, the plant switches on the final step in the production line – to convert the precursors into the toxins – only when it is physically attacked. Kessler believes that this chemical eavesdropping on the misfortunes of other plants is widespread in the green community.

How does brain size compare with brain power?

'Size matters,' some say, but in the context of a developing child's brain, a larger quantity of grey matter evidently does not mean a higher intelligence. In the first study of its kind, researcher Peter Shaw from the US Institute of Mental Health brain-scanned more than three hundred children several times as they grew up, starting from the age of six, and then compared each of the brain scans with the children's IQ tests. The results came as something of a surprise. The scans were designed to look at the sizes of different parts of the brain, and specifically the thickness of the cerebral cortex – the so-called 'grey matter' long associated with intelligence (particularly by one Hercule Poirot).

Unexpectedly, the researchers found that the brightest children very often started with the least amount of grey matter, but then very quickly added much more until the age of eleven, before losing it again in adolescence. These changes were particularly marked in the prefrontal area – the region of the brain associated with reasoning, abstract thought and planning. So, it appears that the rate at which the brain can rearrange or reorganise its cortex, rather than the total amount of grey matter, seems to be the strongest determinant of how clever an individual will be. 'People with very agile minds tend to have a very agile cortex,' Shaw points out.

ZOOLOGY

Can't we genetically modify mosquitoes to become vegetarians? Please?

Researchers at Ohio State University have tracked down some of the key genes responsible for a female mosquito's vampire-like taste for blood. During the summer months, when female mosquitoes lay eggs, they tend to feed on protein-rich blood. But as winter approaches they switch to consuming sugars collected from fruits in order to provide energy stores that enable them to survive during the winter. The trigger for this diet switch turns out to be the length of the day: as the number of hours of daylight declines, heralding the approach of winter, the insects start to bulk up for hibernation.

By comparing which genes were active when the insects were drinking blood versus when they were consuming sugars, scientists David Denlinger and Rebecca Robich pinpointed three genes – two blood-digesting genes and a sugar- and fat-metabolising gene – that appeared to underlie the diet switch. Ultimately, by understanding how these genes control the insects' behaviour, Denlinger and Robich hope to work out a way to use them to develop new methods for controlling mosquitoes (and the diseases they spread) as well as preventing them from making such a meal of us in future.

A tasty prospect: chocolate that lowers cholesterol

In 2003 the Mars confectionery company unveiled the CocoaVia™ range of snacks and bars with the aim of turning on its head the notion that chocolate is not part of a healthy diet. The new products were laced with plant sterols derived from soy which have been shown to be effective at reducing cholesterol levels.

In a study ahead of the launch of the first CocoaVia bar, seventy people with high cholesterol were randomly allocated to eat either two of the new cholesterol-reducing bars a day or two placebo chocolate bars lacking any soy extracts. At the end of the six-week study period, compared with volunteers receiving the placebo chocolate snacks, study subjects eating the new bars had reduced their total cholesterol levels by nearly 5 per cent, and their 'bad' cholesterol (LDL) levels by 6 per cent. Critically, the levels of 'good' cholesterol, known as HDL, remained the same. None of the subjects in either arm of the study showed any changes in weight or blood pressure as a consequence of their chocolate-enhanced lifestyle. And although a 5 per cent reduction in cholesterol doesn't sound like much, it could make the difference between a person's having to use cholesterol-lowering medication or not, particularly in combination with other cholesterol-lowering strategies like diet and weight loss. The chocolate recipe also included high levels of artery-protecting flavanols, a class of antioxidants responsible for the health benefits associated with red wine, green tea and green vegetables.

According to the manufacturer, this was the first time that the combination of plant sterols and flavonoid antioxidants had been offered in a snack bar. Encouraging though this sounds, especially for the average chocoholic, Mars withdrew the brand in 2009 and appears to have replaced it with a new product called Cirku, which, the company suggests on its website, 'helps to maintain good circulation', a rather strange statement, especially as it is accompanied by the rider: 'This statement has not been evaluated by the Food and Drug Administration. This product is not intended to diagnose, treat, cure, or prevent any disease.' Apart from addiction to chocolate, perhaps?

How do you guard against stolen car keys being used to steal your car ?

Car manufacturer DaimlerChrysler has come up with a security system to prevent stolen car keys from being used. Three radio receivers are plumbed the car in three different places. When the 'unlock' button is pressed on the key fob, the signal therefore takes a fractionally different amount of time to reach each receiver. This means users can 'personalise' the system by choosing a highly specific position in which to stand outside the car to unlock it. The receivers log how long the signals take to reach them and thereafter the car will unlock only from that point. Would-be thieves who don't know the correct position will be unable to unlock the car or deactivate the immobiliser.

Weight training without the weights

California-based inventor William Dworzan has come up with a clever way to stay trim on holiday without the problem of carting dumb-bells and weights around with you. His invention comprises a thin rod with handles at each end and a battery-powered gyroscope in the middle. An electric motor spins the gyroscope, which holds the rod steady in a horizontal position. Because it takes a lot of effort to twist the gyroscopically balanced rod from its horizontal position, it can be used as a heavy exercise device – all the workout without the weight.

Can you determine the sex of a dinosaur?

Researchers in the USA have devised a way to work out the sex of a dinosaur – something that was previously impossible. The discovery hinges on the dinosaurs' closest living relatives: birds. As egg layers, female birds need a large reserve of calcium to put into their eggshells, so calcium stores are laid down as an extra layer of bone on the insides of the birds' long bones. When the female needs a calcium boost, the minerals are quickly released from the bones into the bloodstream. This adaptation is absent from male birds because it is driven by the presence of female hormones, chiefly oestrogen. This led North Carolina State University in Raleigh researcher Mary Schweitzer to wonder whether the same might be true of dinosaurs. In 2005, while examining the well-preserved skeleton of a *Tyrannosaurus rex*, she was able to identify bone formations in the fossils very similar to those seen in female birds, suggesting that female dinosaurs also locked away their egg-laying calcium reserves in specialised bone structures. This finding means dinosaur experts now have an objective way to sex the specimens they collect.

 FACTOID:

'If a child does not like eating vegetables, it may be because he or she is genetically programmed to dislike the taste.'

TRUE

According to recent research, 25 per cent of the population are 'supertasters' and carry a gene that produces an increased number of taste buds on the tongue, causing them to dislike the bitter taste of brassicas (like cabbage, sprouts and broccoli) and young tomatoes.

But as well as demonstrating gender, it shows that dinosaurs reproduced very similarly to birds today. 'It indicates that dinosaurs produced and shelled their eggs much more like modern birds than like modern crocodiles,' says Schweitzer.

Is that ancient object genuine?

Researchers have found a way to use X-rays to weed out fake sculptures without harming them. Together with colleagues from France, Italian materials scientist Franco Rustichelli, from the Polytechnic University of the Marche in Ancona, has found that a technique called 'hard X-ray diffraction' can be used to examine the crystal structures of metal and ceramic items, providing information about the casting process and composition of an artefact. By comparing this information with a database of known items it is possible to date objects, and also to weed out fakes which, quite literally, break the mould.

The technique works by shining a beam of high-energy X-rays at the object under scrutiny. The X-rays bounce off the crystals inside the object and then interfere with each other, producing a 'fingerprint' pattern related to the crystal architecture of the artefact. Objects that date from a similar period in history, or that were formed through a specific manufacturing process, have very similar crystal X-ray fingerprints, whereas forgeries show a different pattern altogether.

To prove the point, the researchers tested two bronze castings, a Late Dynastic (1000–300 BC) ancient Egyptian statuette and an Etruscan figurine thought to date from 300 BC. The technique clearly distinguished between the two objects. A major benefit is that previous analyses of this type would have required the physical removal of a fragment of material from an artefact; with this method, the items remain unharmed.

ANIMAL BIOLOGY

If a champion horse has been castrated, can it still breed?

Yes – if you clone it first! Pieraz-Cryozootech-Stallion – Pieraz 2 for short – is genetically identical to Pieraz, a gelded (castrated) Arab horse which won the World Endurance Championship in 1994 and 1996. Critically, unlike his forebear, the cloned Pieraz is also anatomically intact, which means the owners have been able to use him for breeding purposes.

The successful cloning attempt was carried out using cells collected from the original Pieraz in 2002 and stored in liquid nitrogen. Following an agreement between the horse's owner Valerie Kanavy, Paris-based biotech company Cryozootech and Italian breeding company CIZ (which produced the world's first cloned horse, Prometea, in 2003) the same technique that was used to create Dolly the sheep – involving inserting the DNA from one of Pieraz's cells into an egg cell from another horse – was employed to produce Pieraz 2. So far the initiative appears to have been a success because on 5 May 2008 Pieraz 2's first offspring, a healthy filly called Pierazade du Vialaret, was born!

Tch. That is so unfair . . .

Professor David Skuse from Imperial College, London, has found a reason why teenagers make their parents' lives a misery: around the time of puberty they lose their ability to interpret facial expressions. By showing children aged seven to seventeen pictures of faces bearing different expressions and asking the volunteers to comment on the likely mood of the person in the photo, Professor Skuse and his team have found a significant dip in the children's scores around the time of puberty. Females traditionally always outperform males in this task, but the same result was seen among subjects of both sexes. The researchers now want to test a group of children over a number of years as they go through puberty in order to track any changes in their brains using a brain scanner, in order to work out why the effect occurs – and to shed light on how the brain decodes what others are thinking.

Box-office smash or cinematic disaster?

Predicting whether a movie will be a box-office block-buster or a miserable flop can make the difference between business success and financial ruin for producers and promoters, but it has traditionally been a difficult game to play. Now, though, there is a new tool to help out. Ramesh Sharda from Oklahoma State University has developed an artificial neural network that can sort out what is hot from what is not in the world of film. The system, which was set up using data from 834 films shown between 1998 and 2002, considers seven key movie parameters in order to assign a box-office smash score. These are: the 'star value' of the film (in other words, which actors play the lead roles), the age certificate, the competition (which may be a matter of good or bad luck, depending on what else is released simultaneously), the genre of the flick (if it is about French history, for example, it may go down well at Cannes but nowhere else), the special effects, how many screens it will be shown on, and whether it is a sequel. The system uses this data to assign the film to one of nine categories, ranging from 'flop', grossing less than $1 million, to 'blockbuster', taking over $200 million. According to Sharma, his system gets the revenue category absolutely right 37 per cent of the time, and it is correct to within one category either side at least 75 per cent of the time. Directors everywhere must be terrified . . .

Is the Earth's magnetic field about to flip?

The strength of the Earth's magnetic field has decreased by 10 per cent over the last 150 years, raising the possibility that it might be about to collapse and reverse, so that the South Pole becomes the magnetic North Pole. At the current rate of decline our magnetic field could vanish within 1500 to 2000 years before re-establishing itself with the poles reversed. This is not a new phenomenon – the Earth has been flipping its magnetic field about every 100,000–200,000 years – but the last flip was over 800,000 years ago, so we are well overdue for it to happen again. But scientists are sceptical that it will come to that at the moment – although over the southern Atlantic Ocean, a continued weakening of the magnetic field has diminished the shielding effect it has locally in protecting the Earth from the natural radiation that bombards our planet from space. As a result, satellites in low-Earth orbit are left vulnerable to that radiation as they pass over the region known as the South Atlantic Anomaly. Among the satellites that have fallen prey to the harmful effects was one from Denmark designed, ironically, to measure the Earth's magnetic field. The weakening of our magnetic field may also contribute to the loss of our protective ozone layer, which shields us from cancer-causing ultraviolet rays.

MEDICINE

Bag for the heart arrests cardiac failure

Among patients who develop heart failure, the heart enlarges and begins to pump much less efficiently. Reducing the size of the heart, or preventing it from becoming enlarged in the first place, can lead to improvements in heart function. But how can the size of the heart be reduced?

One approach that has shown promise is a device made by the US company Acorn Cardiovascular Inc. and called the CorCap Cardiac Support Device. This is effectively the cardiac equivalent of a string bag. Made from polyester mesh, the device is surgically implanted around the heart to prevent it from enlarging.

A trial involving three hundred heart-failure patients carried out by St Louis University cardiologist Paul Hauptman found that the 148 patients who received the 'heart jacket' improved significantly. According to Hauptman, 'there was a clear improvement in the size and shape of the heart, returning it to a more normal configuration'.

The brain-wave-reading alarm clock knows when to wake you up

Tired of waking up feeling like you haven't even been to bed? Then a new alarm clock that reads your brain waves to pinpoint the best time to wake you up – so that (in theory, at least) you rise feeling fresh and raring to go – could be for you. Sleepsmart, as it is known, was the brainchild of students at Brown University in Rhode Island. It works on the principle that if people are woken up when they are in the lightest phase of sleep, they feel much more alert than if they are woken from deep sleep. So users wear a soft headband in bed which enables the clock to monitor brain activity and pick the right moment to wake you up.

Slugs (and vampires) watch out!

Scientists at Newcastle University have found that garlic can be used to rid your garden of slugs and snails without risking the health of your dogs, cats or other animals that might accidentally eat the traditional slug pellets. The researchers took a leaf out of the books of medieval monks who used to grow garlic close to their crops because they knew it would ward off pests. Now Ingo Schuder and Gordon Port, who carried out the research, have found that spraying Chinese cabbage leaves with garlic extract prevented them from being eaten, and killed many of the slugs and snails that tried.

Plants could also be protected by spraying the extract on to surrounding soil, which stopped pests reaching the crops. The obvious benefit of using a natural plant extract like this is that it is much safer than using artificial chemicals. On the other hand there is the possibility that it could alter the flavour of the food, although, depending on personal taste preferences, this might not be such a bad thing!

At the moment the researchers don't know why garlic kills slugs and snails; one theory is that it affects the animals' nervous systems. The next steps will be to find out whether garlic could be used commercially by farmers to protect their crops, and to confirm that garlic will not damage the environment.

Could hibernating bears hold the key to preventing brittle bones?

Black bears seem to be unique among hibernating animals because they have the ability to stop their bones from thinning during their long winter sleep – suggesting that they may hold the key to preventing bone-thinning diseases like osteoporosis in humans. Usually, any period of prolonged inactivity without weight-bearing exercise, including being immobile, elderly or even going into space, can lead to significant bone loss. But by studying the metabolism of hibernating bears, Seth Donahue and his colleagues from Michigan Technological University have found that, unlike people and other animals, bears keep laying down new bone even when they are inactive. The researchers think this is because, unlike most hibernating animals, bears do not periodically awaken to urinate or defecate, so they have no way to get rid of waste calcium from the body; instead, they put it back into their bones. To find out how they do this, the researchers are now looking for differences between humans and bears among some of the key hormones that regulate bone density and calcium metabolism. This may lead to new therapies for the prevention or reversal of human bone loss. Osteoporosis is a serious problem: around 50 per cent of women and 25 per cent of men over the age of fifty suffer a fracture because of it.

 FACTOID:

'All metals can be magnetised, even precious metals like gold and silver.'

FALSE

Gold cannot be magnetised.

Can we make gadgets more energy-sensible?

A UK-based not-for-profit company, Dynamic Demand, has come up with a way to make appliances less energy-hungry at times when the national power grid struggles to keep up with demand. Their strategy involves giving appliances the ability to monitor how much load the grid is experiencing, and then to cut power usage when things look sticky. The system is elegantly simple: it merely involves monitoring the frequency of the electricity arriving in homes and offices, which is kept close to fifty hertz (cycles per second). When energy demand becomes high, however, the turbines in power stations slow down very slightly, dropping the frequency to, say, 49.5 hertz. Dynamic Demand exploits this drop to enable power-hungry gadgets like air conditioners, boilers or other non-essential items to switch themselves off, or temporarily drop their power rating.

At the moment national grids across the world run a series of standby generators which can power up and down to help smooth out spikes in demand, but keeping them running uses large amounts of energy, is inefficient and produces large amounts of carbon dioxide as a result. The Dynamic Demand approach could help to change all that. As a result, the organisation is now lobbying Parliament, calling for the UK government to take the technology seriously and provide incentives to make its introduction worthwhile.

THE BRAIN

A brain centre for sarcasm? Yeah, right!

Researchers from Israel's University of Haifa have homed in on the part of the brain responsible for comprehending sarcasm. Simone Shamay-Tsoory and her colleagues compared the abilities of forty-one patients with brain injuries and seventeen healthy individuals to understand sarcastic comments. Among the brain-injured patients, twenty-five had damage to the front-most part of the brain, known as the prefrontal cortex, whereas the other sixteen had damage to structures further back in the brain. The patients with damage to the prefrontal cortex, and particularly to the region known as the right ventromedial prefrontal cortex (just above the right eye), had the most difficulty understanding sarcastic remarks. This finding fits with what we already know about this part of the brain, which seems to be heavily involved in complex social interactions, personality and pragmatic language-processing.

ZOOLOGY

How happy is your dog?

People curious about what mood their dog is in can purchase a 'wagometer' which analyses the wag of the tail to determine whether the dog is happy or not. The device is a small sensor strapped to a dog's tail that measures the number of tail wags, as well as their speed and vigour. This data is combined with observations made by the owner of their dog's posture, expression and tail height while wagging; the wagometer then pronounces its verdict. According to the inventor of the device, Dr Roger Mugford, a happy dog tends to have a wide and horizontal wag.

Handling explosives makes your breath smell

Anti-terror squads could soon have a new weapon at their disposal to help track down bombers: a breathalyser that can pick up signs of handling explosives. Dubbed Heartsbreath, the new device – which has been developed by Michael Phillips and his colleagues from Menssana Research in New Jersey – is said to be a billion times more sensitive than the ordinary breathalyser used by traffic cops, and can detect minute traces of explosive compounds exhaled on the breath of individuals who have recently handled ordnance, including dynamite, TNT and C-4.

The machine was originally developed to assist in medical diagnosis, looking for volatile compounds produced by lung cancers and in cases of incipient heart-transplant rejection. But because explosive chemicals can be inhaled or absorbed through the skin, the developers wondered whether the machine could pick up these chemical signatures, too. The researchers admit there is some way to go before this approach becomes a front-line tool in the war against terrorism, but they are optimistic that it could provide a rapid and sensitive way to flush out would-be bombers, possibly including picking up signs of radiation exposure.

Where do new species come from?

Ever since Darwin penned his famous book *On the Origin of Species*, scientists have been searching for evidence that one of his suggestions – that a new species might originate alongside an existing one – is true. While it is well accepted that new species come along when geography intervenes and separates one group of organisms from another (so that, over time, the two populations become genetically distinct from one another), examples of Darwin's other suggestion have not been forthcoming – until now. Two papers – one looking at palm trees on an island off Australia, and the other looking at fish living in a crater lake in Nicaragua – have proved that Darwin was absolutely right (again).

Researcher Vincent Savolainen from Kew Gardens in London found that two species of palm tree on Lord Howe Island, off the south-east coast of the Australian mainland, are genetically very close relatives and must have split away from each other *after* they arrived at the island group. The two tree species prefer slightly different soil types and now flower at different times of the year. Meanwhile, in the Nicaraguan crater lake, Konstanz University's Axel Meyer has found a unique species of cichlid fish alongside a close relative. That the unique species was not found in any other lake they tested, and prefers to live in open water compared with its shore-loving relative, proves that the fish must have evolved recently (within the last ten thousand years or less) side by side with its relatives. Aside from permitting Darwin a smug grin in his grave, and settling a 150-year-old argument, these findings have implications for our understanding of how new species emerge, including human ones.

Ants can cultivate some trees and kill others

Scientists have solved the mystery of a strange phenomenon in the Amazon known as Devil's Gardens: large tracts of rainforest that contain just a single species of tree; any other plant that tries to grow quickly withers and dies. But far from being the work of evil spirits, as local legends had suggested, the cause, Stanford University scientist Megan Frederickson discovered, is actually a species of ant with a penchant for cultivating a certain type of tree. *Myrmelachista schumanni*, the scientific name for the ants, build their nests in the hollow stems of a tree called *Duroia hirsute*. And to ensure a ready supply of nesting sites in the future, they actively poison all the other plants in the vicinity, leaving just their preferred species of tree alive. Initially, scientists had thought that the tree itself might be preventing the growth of other nearby species, but when the researchers planted saplings of a different species in their midst they found that the ants promptly turned on the impostors and killed them by injecting formic acid from their stings into the leaves.

 FACTOID:

'If all the passengers on an aircraft suddenly jumped up off the floor, the plane would very briefly weigh less.'

FALSE

The weight of the plane would very briefly *increase*, because of the force exerted on the floor of the aircraft by the passengers in the act of jumping.

Infectious therapy for haemophilia

US researchers have successfully used gene therapy to treat a group of human sufferers with one form of the bleeding disorder haemophilia. The University of Pennsylvania's Catherine Manno and her colleagues used a genetically modified virus to add a working version of a gene for the blood-clotting protein called Factor IX, which is missing from the blood of patients with this form of the condition, known as haemophilia B. The team used an agent called an 'adeno-associated virus' from which they had removed the normal viral genetic material and replaced it with a copy of the human Factor IX gene. The modified virus was injected into the hepatic artery – which supplies blood to the liver – in seven patients. The viral particles were then carried into the liver, where they entered a number of liver cells and inserted their clotting-gene cargo into the patients' DNA. Encouragingly, the patients that received the highest viral doses began to produce detectable levels of Factor IX in their blood, restoring normal blood-clotting, although the effect persisted for only two months. The researchers believe that this was the consequence of the immune system removing the liver cells that had been infected by the virus, suggesting that longer treatment might be possible if drugs are given to control the immune system.

Significantly, this study proves that a modified virus can be used safely to deliver therapeutic genes to the liver, potentially sparing haemophiliacs the inconvenience of daily injections with costly blood-clotting replacements.

Blogging for aliens

Blogging is now mainstream, and even a full-time profession for some prolific and digitally well-endowed writers. But as this nascent means of online self-expression began to establish itself in the early noughties, investors everywhere, recognising its potential, began hunting for cunning ways to sign up potential bloggers. Among them was a Florida-based social networking company, Mindcomet, which went a step further with the launch of a free service to beam blogs into space. Ostensibly concerned that extraterrestrials might get a bad impression of humankind from the (often) atrocious TV and radio transmissions that we are unleashing on any alien eavesdroppers, the idea was to present our species in a more favourable light to any aliens out there who might be listening. Naturally, contributors to blogsinspace.com, as it was known, were urged to refrain from using any language or content that might offend off-world recipients . . .

Seeing the universe's first stars

One of the universe's first stars, which was shining over 12.8 billion years ago, just eight hundred million years after the Big Bang, has been spotted by researchers from the USA, Europe and Japan. With the help of the SWIFT Swift satellite, a joint UK, Italian and American initiative launched in 2004 to track gamma-ray bursts (GRBs), which occur when stars explode, in 2005 researchers including the University of North Carolina's Dan Reichart and the Tokyo Institute of Technology's Nobuyaki Kawai spotted a GRB mapping to a massive stellar convulsion that took place nearly thirteen billion years ago. By analysing the light emitted from the explosion, the researchers were able to determine that the star was a giant of at least thirty times the mass of our own sun, and had created a rich supply of oxygen, silicon and metals that had been released to provide the raw materials for complex chemistry in future worlds and stars. The discovery makes this early star one of the most distant ever sighted, and has shed further light on our understanding of the early universe.

FACTOID:

'Inexorable continental drift means that Britain and North America are separating from each other by about twenty-five millimetres a year.'

FALSE

They are moving apart, but only by about ten millimetres a year – about the same rate that your fingernails grow over the same period.

Did the death of a star alter human evolution?

A team of German scientists examining material from the seabed beneath the Pacific Ocean think they may have uncovered explosive evidence of an event that altered the evolution of humankind. Drilling 4800 metres below the surface, Günther Korschinek and his colleagues from the Munich Technical University discovered a band of deposits dating back about three million years and containing a rare form of iron called iron-60. This is normally produced only during the death throes of stars as they explode in a process called a supernova. The discovery of these rare iron deposits on Earth therefore indicates that a star must have exploded within 100–200 light-years of Earth, peppering the planet shortly after with the iron-rich debris. At the same time, the Earth would also have seen a surge in cosmic radiation for at least a hundred thousand years, which could have significantly increased cloud cover, altering the climate. Temperatures would have dropped, causing the polar ice-caps to expand and leading to a drier climate in Africa, a suggestion supported by records of past climate written into ancient rock-cores. This change in climate, argues Korschinek, could have been the driving force that encouraged early humans to adapt and spread out, as the trees receded and the African savannah opened up.

MEDICINE

Why cigarettes and coffee are a killer combination

Greek researchers have found that the habit of starting the day with a coffee and a cigarette may be extra hard on your arteries. Dr Charalambos Vlachopoulos from the Athens Medical School – a man who has also investigated the health-giving properties of chocolate – studied the arterial stiffness of twenty-four young, healthy adults when they smoked a cigarette, drank a cup of coffee, or did both. The study showed that the combination of caffeine and smoking made the body's main blood vessel – the aorta, which leads directly from the heart to supply the rest of the body – temporarily stiffer than either drug alone, or the two added together. In other words, the effects of the two drugs together multiply rather than add up, and may contribute to increased harm to the arteries in the long term.

Indeed, a second, larger study involving 160 adults found that those who were regular cigarette and coffee consumers showed the greatest blood-vessel stiffness. Stiffer blood vessels elevate blood pressure, making the heart work harder to push blood around the body, and therefore increase the risk of heart disease and stroke.

PSYCHOLOGY

Teams wearing red are more likely to win

Scientists have found that the world-famous Manchester United would do better if they always played in red (although this is impossible, given the Football Association's current insistence on different home and away strips) because they would be statistically much more likely to win. Robert Barton and Russell Hill from Durham University analysed the outcomes of four combat sports from the Athens 2004 Olympics – boxing, tae kwon do, Graeco-Roman wrestling and freestyle wrestling – and found that participants competing in red were significantly and consistently more likely to win against opponents clad in blue. Analysis of a series of games from Euro 2004 also turned up the same results.

The researchers put the findings down to redness being a testosterone-fuelled masculine signal used throughout nature as a sign of dominance, anger, danger and aggression. Fear, on the other hand, is associated more with a bluish pallor. Red-clad competitors may therefore be influencing a primitive part of their opponents' brain that is programmed to be awed by redness, leading to a psychological disadvantage in the blue-bedecked opponent. Tough, then, Manchester City fans!

GENE THERAPY

Making a cell see

In a move that might help to overcome some forms of blindness, scientists have made cells grown in a dish become light-sensitive by switching on just one gene. Imperial College, London, researcher Mark Hankins and his colleagues made the discovery when they activated a gene that enables cells to make a substance called melanopsin. This chemical responds to light at the blue end of the spectrum, so when the cells were illuminated with light of the right colour they altered their activity, indicating that they had been made light-sensitive. Melanopsin is normally used by a special group of cells in the retina whose job it is to distinguish night from day in order to set the brain's 'body clock'. But this study shows that, in theory, it's possible to make almost any cell light-sensitive; this means that, while not specifically indicating a potential cure for blindness, this technique could none the less lead to new treatments for certain forms of sight loss, including retinitis pigmentosa, a hereditary condition that causes the destruction of the retinal rods and cones, the light-sensitive cells that turn light waves into brain waves.

HUMAN BIOLOGY

Men really do do more stupid things when there's a pretty woman around

It's often claimed that men just can't help showing off in front of women, whether it's at the wheel of a car, behind the barbecue or on a surfboard, and almost always with disastrous consequences. Now new research from Australia confirms this is indeed the case and lays the blame firmly at the feet of the macho-male hormone testosterone. University of Queensland researchers Bill von Hippel and Richard Ronay found that male skateboarders execute more high-risk and daring manoeuvres, accompanied by significantly more crash landings, when they are watched by an attractive female, compared with when they have a male audience. Saliva tests also revealed a surge in testosterone whenever a good-looking woman was around. According to von Hippel, it's all part of a 'sexual display strategy' aimed at impressing a potential mate. It's a shame, then, that previous research from the US suggests that these days women actually prefer more cautious consorts for potential mates. So maybe ditch the fast car for something sensible, and see if your luck changes.

Japanese scientists fill a gap in our knowledge of tooth repair

Comforting news: dental researchers have developed a new material for fillings that greatly reduces any need for the dentist's drill. The cement-like amalgam equivalent latches on to damaged tooth surfaces and integrates itself seamlessly into the tooth structure, producing an invisible mend.

Tooth decay occurs when acid produced by mouth bacteria eats into the enamel surfaces of teeth, producing small pits. Dentists currently have to enlarge the hole, drilling away healthy tooth material, in order to provide a secure socket for the filling material because it does not adhere perfectly to the enamel surface. But the new material is a paste made of hydroxyapatite – a form of calcium phosphate, exactly the same substance that makes up the enamel itself. When the paste is added to a damaged tooth, it sets within minutes, sealing off the affected area and bonding immaculately to the tooth surface. The repair is invisible even when viewed under a microscope.

Lead author in the study, Kazue Yamagishi from the FAP Dental Institute in Tokyo, points out that, because the paste is quite acidic, it initially dissolves some of the native tooth enamel before forming new crystals which lock themselves into the tooth surface in a smooth, homogeneous layer. The method not only repairs decayed teeth but can strengthen them, preventing the problem from recurring.

ROBOTS

The self-cloning robot

Scary as it sounds, US researchers have produced a robot that can make functional copies of itself. The robot consists of a series of identical cubes that can rotate about their diagonals and selectively stick to each other using electro-magnets. In much the same way that most human cells carry a complete copy of their DNA genome, each of the robot's cubes comes complete with a computer program telling it how to co-operate with other cubes to form a robot and replicate. Given a ready supply of food (more of the same cubes), the robot can build a copy of itself. Although this robot has no specific application, it is an important proof of the concept, which developer Hod Lipson of Cornell University says he hopes will pave the way for the production of robots capable of self-assembly and repair for use in space or other extreme environments.

 FACTOID:

'Mice are super-intelligent – on forays in unfamiliar territory they leave trails in order to find their way back safely and quickly.'

TRUE

Scientists at Oxford University have found that mice often leave piles of seeds, twigs or shells to help them find their way home in confusing places like large fields of crops. Leaving visual signals like this is thought to be safer than scent-marking, which a predator could pick up.

Dolphins use tools

In a marine first, scientists have discovered that some of the dolphins that live in Shark Bay, Western Australia, have learned to use 'tools' to help them catch fish. At least twenty-five of the animals have been spotted 'sponging', as the practice has become known, which involves wearing conically shaped whole sponges, which they tear off the sea bottom, on the ends of their noses. This equips them with the marine equivalent of a hard-hat to protect their noses while they forage on the seabed.

Interestingly, the dolphins involved in the practice seem to be overwhelmingly female, and appear to be passing the idea on to their daughters. And the males? According to Dr Michael Krützen, who first described the sponging behaviour while working at the University of New South Wales, the males are too busy foraging for females to waste time poking around on the seabed. Clearly, dolphins are a lot more like humans than we give them credit for.

Memory-eroding junk food . . .

Scientists have shown that eating fatty food not only clogs up your blood vessels but is bad for your brain. Rats fed the rodent equivalent of high-fat junk food for two months were less mentally agile and had significantly worse memories compared with normally nourished animals. The rats were tested on their abilities to find their way around mazes, and to locate platforms hidden just below the surface of a pool of water. According to Medical University of South Carolina researcher Ann-Charlotte Granholm, who carried out the study, animals on high-fat diets took much longer to learn the tasks, and made many more mistakes, than their healthier counterparts.

Other scientists looking into this question blame the poor performance of junk-food-fed rats on high bloodstream levels of triglycerides, a type of fat, because when John Morley, a researcher at VA Medical Center in St Louis, gave a group of affected animals a triglyceride-lowering drug, their memories improved. Memory problems similar to those experienced by the rats have also been documented in humans with diabetes and high triglyceride levels, although it remains to be seen whether the same is true in healthy human subjects.

But the researchers do point out, in the meantime,

that raised triglyceride levels in humans are all too commonly caused by the presence of trans-fatty acids, which are popular with food manufacturers because they prolong a product's shelf-life. So steer clear of the junk food and grab a salad instead – if you can remember to . . .

Viral voltages to diagnose infections

Scientists from Harvard University have devised a detector which can rapidly identify some viruses in patient samples, based on their electrical behaviour. Charles Lieber and his team have found a way to link tiny silicon wires, so small as to be described as nanowires, to antibodies that can lock on to specific viruses. When the antibodies lock on to the virus they recognise, or even just a fragment of that virus, the electrical conductance of the wires changes in a characteristic way for that particular virus. In other words, different viruses produce their own specific electrical fingerprints, which enable the machine immediately to identify which viruses are present in a sample collected from a patient. So far the technique has worked successfully on flu viruses, adenoviruses and a member of the mumps virus family.

The major benefit is the speed with which the machine can help a doctor reach a diagnosis. Present methods involve sending samples to a laboratory where they are painstakingly cultured, subjected to DNA analysis or identified under the microscope, often with the aid of colour-coded antibodies. The whole process is very labour-intensive and time-consuming. The new nanowire technique can also detect several different infections simultaneously, again saving time, and patients receive appropriate treatment for their infections more rapidly – including being isolated from other patients to whom they might pose an infection risk.

Plants that glow in the dark to get noticed

A group of Spanish researchers has found that certain night-blooming flowers might have another 'trick up their leaves' to attract certain pollinators, such as bees and bats: the ability to glow in the dark. Fernando Gandia-Herrero and his colleagues at the University of Murcia in Spain extracted the pigments from *Mirabilis jalapa* flowers and found that one of them – yellow betaxanthin – can soak up blue light and use the energy to make itself glow green. The petals of the plant also create alluring patterns by adding (apparently only in certain places) a second substance, called betanin, which can nullify the fluorescence to make those parts of the leaf look dark. Budgerigars and shrimps are known to set high store by the fluorescence of their partners, but this is the first time that a plant has been found to resort to the floral equivalent of a fluorescent jacket to get noticed in the mating game.

 FACTOID:

'A person with an IQ of 100 is rather more intelligent than average.'

FALSE

An IQ of 100 is intended precisely to represent the average intelligence. People with an IQ below 100 are accordingly said to have below-average intelligence, and those with an IQ above 100 are said to be of above-average intelligence.

HUMAN BIOLOGY

Can you fool an egg into thinking it's been fertilised?

The therapeutic potential of stem cells for humans is huge, but many people object, on the grounds that embryos are often required to produce them. But now Karl Swann and his team from the University of Cardiff have found a way to fool unfertilised eggs into thinking that they have been fertilised by a sperm, so that they begin the process of cell division and hence stem-cell production.

The key to the trick involves injecting the egg with an enzyme from sperm called phospholipase C-zeta (PLC-zeta). Normally, the sperm carries this enzyme into the egg, signalling fertilisation, but because no sperm have been used, the egg contains only DNA from the mother and hence cannot turn into a baby, which should allay the fears of people concerned about the ethics of using embryos as a source of human 'spare parts'. Another potential spin-off of the project is the possibility that it might help people trying to become pregnant by in-vitro fertilisation (IVF). Very often, embryos created by fertilising eggs with sperm in a test-tube fail to begin to divide, possibly because the sperm have defective PLC-zeta. Adding the enzyme artificially might help to kick-start division, boosting the chances of IVF success.

A robotic replacement for guide dogs

Engineers at the University of Utah have come up with an electronic guide dog which takes cues from hidden beacons concealed in the environment to help visually impaired people find their way around foreign environments, such as airports, or locate the right shelves in shops; in other words, in situations in which a normal guide dog would be less helpful. Developed by computer-science professor Vladimir Kulyukin, the robot accepts a destination selected by the user from a Braille directory, and he or she is at once escorted directly there. Upon arrival the 'dog' can then provide more specialised information – such as where to find the toothpaste on a grocery-store shelf. Sachin Pavithran, a visually impaired test subject for the project, said, 'When I am in an airport and have a flight layover, I am often stuck in one place because I can't get around by myself. This robot would give me back some independence.'

Controlling crowds by microwave

US defence researchers have developed a vehicle-mounted microwave weapon designed to 'cook' crowds into submission. The 'active denial system', also known as the 'pain ray', fires a narrow microwave beam at a frequency of ninety-five gigahertz over a range of seven hundred metres. When the beam hits flesh, it rapidly heats the skin, triggering intense pain and encouraging the target to move away. According to reports, a two-second burst from the device can heat the skin surface to 50° Celsius, producing excruciating pain but with little risk of permanent harm. The idea is that the discomfort should persuade would-be troublemakers to disperse. And even if it doesn't work as a crowd dispersant, perhaps would-be cannibals will be interested in the boil-in-the-bag prospects of the technology . . .

New solution for effective crowd control – a laser stun-gun

Meanwhile, the US military have been developing a laser stun-gun capable of inflicting paralysis and excruciating pain on anyone unlucky enough to be within its two-kilometre range. This class of weapon, known as a 'pulsed energy projectile' or PEP, is intended as a crowd-control measure to 'neutralise' rioters. It emits a powerful laser beam which generates a charged plasma cloud whenever it hits someone. The expanding plasma over-excites the nervous system, triggering severe pain sensations as well as temporary paralysis. However, the researchers working on the project have struggled to optimise the system so that it produces pain without the other major side-effects: death and debilitating life-long states of agony! Consequently, neuroscientists around the world have breathed a collective sigh of relief that the project has now been shelved. Many were horrified over the potential effects of using such a weapon, which could include life-long pain syndromes that might be triggered if the stun-gun caused the nervous system to 'rewire' itself.

So is that it for the PEP? Apparently not. Although the US military have announced that they are not pursuing the crowd-control angle, they say they 'will leverage the work accomplished in the PEP project for other potential initiatives', which apparently means turning the laser system into a weapon for shooting down unmanned aerial vehicles.

HUMAN BIOLOGY

Asian flu is highly infectious – but what about Asian laughter?

Concerned about surging levels of depression among the seven million residents of Hong Kong, in mid-July 2005 the Joyful Mental Health Foundation organised a laughing contest in the city to raise people's spirits. Contestants were judged on how long they could laugh, and the effect of their laughter on others. According to one of the organisers, the judges were instructed to look for 'the quality of the laughter, whether it is infectious, and genuine'. In Britain such exercises are unnecessary – we merely have to look at the size of the average worker's wage relative to a banker's bonus to provoke a paroxysm of helpless laughter.

The world's biggest battery

Guinness World Records has acknowledged a new contender for the largest battery ever built. Weighing 1300 tonnes, covering an area larger than a football pitch and made up of 13,760 nickel-cadmium cells linked together, ABB-Saft's installation in Alaska is a record breaker. It has been built in Fairbanks as a back-up system for the local power grid, notorious for power cuts, which, with temperatures around –50° Celsius, are no laughing matter.

The new battery, christened BESS (battery energy storage system), cost $30 million to build, sits in a warehouse near the city and can provide twenty-six megawatts of power for fifteen minutes or heavier demands of up to forty-six megawatts for shorter periods – generally enough to keep ten thousand homes running until normal service is resumed.

Does dwarf planet Pluto have a moon?

Indeed it does; but not just one. Thanks to the sharp eyes of the Hubble Space Telescope, researchers have spotted two additional moons in orbit around the solar system's (now downgraded) outermost planet, Pluto. Excitingly christened S/2005 P1 and S/2005 P2, the new satellites – which orbit at a distance of 48,000–64,000 kilometres from the planet – join Charon, Pluto's first known moon, which is so relatively large as to be virtually a 'companion planet'.

The discovery was announced by researchers Alan Stern and Hal Weaver, who focused Hubble on the area around Pluto and watched as two tiny pinpricks of light came into view. The moons were not spotted before because they are so much smaller than Charon, whose light easily hides their presence. Because all three moons circle Pluto in the same plane, the researchers believe that they all formed together, rather than being the result of Pluto's capturing pieces of passing debris. Exactly how they formed is still something of a mystery, although researchers believe that planet and moons are probably the end result of a cosmic collision between two Pluto-sized objects. To explore these theories further, Weaver and Stern plan to refocus Hubble back on Pluto to look for any other moons and to determine the size, shape and composition of the new discoveries, which should also shed welcome light on how the Plutonian system may have formed.

Going to church makes you eat better

Statisticians have known for some time that people who go to church tend to live longer. But now a new study on churchgoers' eating habits provides one possible explanation as to why: regular church attenders eat more healthily. Deirdre Griffith and her colleagues at the St Louis University School of Public Health compared the diets of frequent worshippers with those of non-churchgoers. They found that people who frequently go to church eat on average 26 per cent more 'powerhouse' fruits and vegetables – those containing the most nutrients – than their less pious counterparts. They say your body is a temple, so it's perhaps unsurprising that going to church apparently helps you to treat it that way!

But it's a little early to conclude that religiously going to church improves your diet – the findings could be biased by any number of different factors. After all, the very exercise and activity of going to church must create a heartier appetite for wholesome food than lazing at home all day snacking and raiding the fridge for packaged meals. Social class in some areas may also be influential, with those in higher social classes, who are known to eat a better diet and live longer, also being more likely to go to church.

FACTOID:

*'The neon of neon tube lighting
is a kind of gas.'*

TRUE

Neon is one of the so-called noble gases and is used in electric lights and signs because when it is excited by electricity it produces a bright and continuous glow.

MEDICINE

Can Alzheimer's symptoms be controlled?

A team of researchers at the University of California, Irvine, led by Professor Frank LaFerla has found a drug capable of halting the progression of Alzheimer's disease in mice genetically programmed to develop the rodent equivalent of the condition. A characteristic feature of Alzheimer's is the loss of a class of nerve cells that use the chemical acetylcholine, one of the brain's key nerve-transmitter substances that conveys information from one neurone to another. The new agent, known as NGX267, is able to mimic this missing transmitter, thereby reducing the symptoms of the disease.

Intriguingly, it also seems to be able to halt the development of two other key pathological characteristics of Alzheimer's: the accumulation of toxic tangles called PHF-tau inside nerve cells and protein aggregates called amyloid plaques. A Californian bio-tech company, TorreyPines Therapeutics, has been conducting a clinical trial to confirm the safety of the agent for use in humans. In early tests the drug appears to have been well tolerated, although it remains to be seen whether it will work as well in humans with dementia as it has done in the Alzheimer's mice.

TECHNOLOGY

Is this the world's most efficient solar power station?

Engineers at Stirling Energy Systems reflecting on the best way to boost energy production in California –

where solar energy already competes with more traditional contributors to the state power grid – have come up with a technological breakthrough called the Sun-Catcher™. Resembling a satellite dish, this comprises an eleven-metre-wide mirrored reflector that tracks the sun throughout the day, focusing its light on to a central 'engine' which contains a series of cylinders filled with hydrogen. The light reflected from the mirror heats the hydrogen to over 700° C, causing it to expand and force down a piston in each cylinder. The falling pistons drive a generator, which produces electricity, and at the same time the hot gas is cooled by a radiator system before being recycled within the engine. The whole process converts solar energy to electrical energy with an efficiency of about 30 per cent – roughly twice as much as that achievable with the best solar (photovoltaic) cells – and each SunCatcher™ dish generates electricity at the rate of twenty-five kilowatts. Currently plans for two electricity-generating plants are on the drawing board: one near Los Angeles, which will produce about five hundred megawatts, and a second outside San Diego, which will pump out up to nine hundred megawatts when completed. Both sites will contain over thirty thousand SunCatcher™ dishes.

The laser breath freshener

Israeli scientists have found a way to banish bad breath for good – with a laser. Most cases of bad breath, or halitosis, result from stinky gases like hydrogen sulphide that are pumped out by bacteria living in crevices between the teeth and at the gum margins. A trip to the dentist, together with careful brushing and flossing, usually solves the problem. But there are some rarer cases (about 6 per cent) which are more difficult to treat, and Yehuda Finkelstein, from the Sapir Medical Centre in Kfar, Israel, having pinpointed the tonsils as the cause, has found that a quick blast with a laser can often remedy the situation.

In these problem cases, bacteria multiply deep within grooves in the tonsils known as crypts. Laser therapy works by abrading the surface of the tonsils, provoking the formation of scar tissue, which seals off the crypts, preventing bacteria from multiplying there. In an initial trial of fifty-three patients, over half were cured following their first treatment and the rest after two or three sessions. However, before you opt for the laser, dentists advise that you try more conventional therapies first – such as scraping your tongue, drinking plenty of water, flossing and careful tooth cleaning.

FACTOID:

'In smoking cigarettes, what may cause cancer is the nicotine.'

FALSE

Nicotine is what makes cigarettes addictive. What might cause cancer is the tars the cigarettes contain, which are produced by burning the tobacco.

ASTRONOMY

Spacecraft lands on asteroid

The Japan Aerospace Exploration Agency has reported that *Hayabusa* – its mission to land on and retrieve a sample from 25143 Itokawa, a 540-metre-long potato-shaped asteroid drifting about three hundred million kilometres from Earth – has been at least partly successful. The craft was launched in May 2003 and arrived in the vicinity of the asteroid in September 2005. But problems with the landing gear meant that, for a while, the success of the mission hung in the balance. However, in November 2005 mission control announced that the probe had fired two metal projectiles into the asteroid's surface to liberate surface particles that were (it is hoped) then collected and stored for the return to Earth. Leaving Itokawa, the probe encountered further technical problems, including engine trouble, but these too were resolved and *Hayabusa* – which means 'peregrine falcon' – arrived home in June 2010, when it parachuted down near Woomera, Australia. With luck, it will have brought with it the first pristine samples ever collected from an asteroid, which should help to shed some fresh light on the nature of the material from which our solar system was formed some 4.5 billion years ago.

The helicopter that flies itself

Israeli firm Steadicopter has recently developed the 35-kilogram, 1.7-metre-long Black Eagle 50, an unmanned helicopter that uses clever computer software and global positioning satellite technology to fly without any human intervention. This means that anyone, trained pilot or not, can control it from a remote location. And if the aircraft loses contact with its operator it can also continue and complete its mission automatically. It can carry three-kilogram payloads on missions lasting up to three hours and is powered by a 116-cc water-cooled engine that can push it along at 126 k.p.h. at altitudes up to 9000 feet (2743 metres).

For those with larger things in mind, Steadicopter also produces a kit to convert a manned helicopter to an unmanned one that will work with any craft from hobby-sized to military. So you might never need to get that pilot's licence.

Is loneliness bad for your health?

In a study of eighty-three male and female first-year university students who were vaccinated against the flu, those who scored most highly on a 'loneliness survey' and had the most restricted social networks mounted the weakest antibody responses, making them more susceptible to the virus than their better-befriended counterparts. According to researcher Sarah Pressman of Carnegie Mellon University in Pittsburgh, who ran the study, these findings could also help to explain why first-year students tend to be ill more often than older students, because they feel socially 'unanchored', making them more susceptible to infection.

Disguised as a poisonous frog

Imitation may be the sincerest form of flattery, but not when it comes to toxicity, it seems. University of Texas researcher Catherine Darst has found that where the ranges of two species of poison-arrow frogs overlap in the Ecuadorian Amazon rainforest, other non-toxic frogs are imitating their bright colour schemes to deceive predators partial to a frog-sized meal into leaving them alone. Stealing the danger signals of others to gain an advantage for yourself is nothing new in nature, but what surprised Darst was that the copycat frogs were disguising themselves as the *less* poisonous of the two toxic frog species.

Why should they not take the apparently obvious option of looking like the more poisonous variety? To find out, she offered young bird chicks a taste of each type of toxic frog. When the birds ate the more poisonous variety of frog, the experience was so unpleasant that it deterred the chicks from trying *any* frog for a period subsequently. But when they sampled the less toxic frog the birds developed a long-lasting aversion specifically to that frog and no other type. So, ingeniously, by imitating the less toxic of the two species, the non-poisonous frogs gain the protection of both species, rather than just one!

What if I want to cross the road and there's no gap in the traffic?

Well, you could always try a Japanese invention in the form of a portable zebra crossing to help you out. It is made of plastic painted with black and white stripes. Apparently, you simply unroll your 'crossing' at a point that suits you and, hey presto, you have a route across the road. That said, the makers do caution that attempting to deploy your crossing on busy roads with no break in the traffic 'might be dangerous' . . .

Can you make yourself smell younger?

A study at the Smell and Taste Treatment and Research Foundation, Chicago, has found that the scent of grapefruit on a woman makes her seem to a man to be up to six years younger than she actually is. (A man with the same scent leaves no equivalent impression on a woman.) Foundation director Alan Hirsch smeared several middle-aged women with an appetising range of plant products, including broccoli, banana, spearmint, grapefruit and lavender, before asking a panel of men to guess their ages. When the women wore grapefruit they were consistently ranked younger than their real ages. The researchers still have no idea why, however.

Are ugly kids less loved by parents?

A Canadian researcher who staked out fourteen super-markets to watch how attentive parents were towards their children found that children he subjectively judged to be 'less attractive-looking' were not so likely to be belted into the supermarket trolley, and were allowed to stray much further away from their parents than their prettier, handsomer peers. In other words, they received less care. University of Alberta scientist Dr Andrew Harrell, who carried out the research, says that it is all down to Darwin: we are unconsciously more likely to lavish attention on attractive children simply because they are the most likely to ensure the continuation of our own family.

Perfect toast every time

Magnetic Design – a company based in Cambridge – has developed a device that, with the help of a little harmless radiation, promises to deliver 'perfect toast every time'. Combining a smoke detector with the heating elements of a toaster, the company's kitchen must-have can tell automatically when it is time to pop up the slice. It has no timer, as such. Instead it works by sucking in particles of caramelised bread vapour, which are released as the toast cooks, and blowing them into a stream of radioactive particles similar to those found in a smoke detector. The toast particles mop up the radioactive particles, reducing the number picked up by an adjacent sensor. The more singed the toast becomes, the more particles it emits, and the greater the amount of radioactivity that gets mopped up before it can reach the sensor. By setting the toaster to switch off when the radioactivity drops to a certain level – dialled in by you – you can guarantee that your toast will always be cooked to your idea of perfection, no matter how brown you like it, and regardless of whether you start with warm, cold or even frozen bread.

Can we use 3D screens without the goggles?

In 2002, the world's first three-dimensional screen was developed by a Massachusetts-based firm called

Actuality Systems. Shaped like a fair-sized goldfish bowl that the user can physically walk around and view from any angle, the screen system faithfully renders images in 3D and in real time. Potential applications include, for example, three-dimensional human body scans and X-rays, as well as the ability to visualise the relative positions of aeroplanes guided by air-traffic controllers. The system, called Perspecta, works by spinning a circular white polymer disc fifteen times per second. Clever computer software chops a 3D computer model into 198 'slices', which are then projected on to the spinning disc in quick succession, fooling the eye into seeing a solid object hovering in space.

 FACTOID:

'When walking, ants move three legs together at a time, keeping the other three on the ground.'

TRUE

They lift a front leg and a hind leg on one side of the body, and the middle leg on the opposite side of the body, keeping the other three on the ground.

Has anyone thought of a way of making text messages less impersonal?

Russian company SeeStorm can make texting far more visually animated by including a moving image of the text messager. The sender first takes a photo of him- or herself and sends it to SeeStorm, which uses software to capture the face of the sender. The company then uses a library of eye and mouth pictures to recreate speaking movements, which are matched appropriately to the words in the text message. The texted person then receives an animated version of the caller – complete with moving mouth and lips – speaking the message.

Recreating Spiderman

A team of US researchers led by Ali Dhinojwala from the University of Akron has managed to recreate the sticky feet of a gecko artificially. Geckos are renowned for their ability to stick to almost any surface, an effect they achieve by having toes covered in tiny hairs called setae, which form electrical attractive forces (known as 'van der Waals attractions') with the underlying surface. The researchers have worked out how to create a carpet of tiny carbon nanotubes with similar properties, but with two hundred times the gripping power of a gecko's foot. Consequently the same thing for a human could be coming soon . . .

Scientists capture a comet, or at least part of it

After a tense wait, on Sunday, 15 January 2006 space scientists breathed a collective sigh of relief when it was confirmed that the *Stardust* probe – launched in February 1999 to gather samples from the comet Wild 2 – had touched down safely in the Utah desert. But the waiting wasn't over: until the probe's collector was opened, no one knew whether it had grabbed anything. Thankfully the mission proved a huge success, and the principal investigator, Washington University's Donald Brownlee, has calculated that there are more than a million microscopic specks of dust embedded in the probe's low-density-glass aerogel collecting system.

The samples will help researchers to piece together the recipe for the stellar soup from which our solar system formed 4.5 billion years ago. Scientists are also inviting the public to muck in and help them dig for the dirt particles by joining the 'stardust@home' project, in which home computers help to sift through images of tiny sections of the collector, looking for more traces of dust from Wild 2.

So far, and surprisingly, a major constituent of the dust has been analysed as olivine – a sort of green sand found on Earth on Hawaiian beaches – although other elements present are the more standard iron, magnesium, calcium, aluminium and titanium. The dust has also revealed that components formed in the inner part of the solar system were mixing far more extensively than previously thought with material from the outer part of the solar system. Understanding how this happened will aid scientists in understanding the finer points of how our cosmic neighbourhood came to be.

EVOLUTION

How did our ears evolve?

Scientists studying the fossilised remains of a strange prehistoric fish have found a missing link in the puzzle of where we got our ears from. Martin Brazeau from the University of Uppsala in Sweden has found that *Panderichthys*, which flopped around in shallow water about 370 million years ago and was the immediate predecessor of the first animals to crawl on to land, had modified one of its gills and turned it into an ear canal. The researchers think that the fish initially adapted its gills in this way to produce a primitive snorkel to help it to breathe comfortably in muddy water, or to prevent it from having to lift its head above water to take a mouthful of air. When its descendants later invaded the land, they capitalised on the new design and completed the picture by adding the remaining parts of the ear system we still use today. Evolution is only very rarely frozen in mid-stride by fossils like this, making this a landmark study – aside from its importance in showing us where we got our ears from.

 FACTOID:

'Like petrol engines, diesel engines rely on spark plugs to ignite the fuel.'

FALSE

Petrol engines use spark plugs, but diesel engines rely on compressing air in the cylinder to make it hot enough to ignite the fuel.

How can bird flu kill, but not spread?

Researchers in the USA and Japan have solved the mystery of why strains of avian flu like H5N1 can infect and kill a human yet spread only very poorly to other people. The answer lies on the surfaces of the cells in the respiratory tract, a study by Yoshihiro Kawaoka of the University of Tokyo has shown. Strains of the flu that infect humans and our close mammalian relatives recognise sugars on the surfaces of our cells which are linked to each other in what is called a 2,6 configuration. Birds, on the other hand, are different and the sugars on their cells are linked in a 2,3 configuration – so avian flu viruses are adapted to reflect this. But when the researchers looked closely at human airways they found that certain cells called type 2 pneumocytes, which are found in the deepest reaches of the lungs, have the 2,3 sugar linkages more normally seen in birds. This means that when H5N1 infects someone, the infection tends to be confined to this cell population deep in the lungs, rather than growing in the upper airways, which is the usual flu hot-spot. This makes it much harder for the virus to escape from the victim in sufficient quantities to infect others. The virus will begin to spread between humans only when it adapts to recognise the normal human sugar configurations. For swine flu, though, we were less lucky because, coming from a pig, the virus arrived ready-adapted to use the mammalian configuration of sugars, so it spread around the world unhindered.

How can I charge my phone on the move?

Engineer Joe Hynek from the University of Iowa has come up with a solar handbag – dubbed the Power Purse – and matching sunhat. The idea is to have about your person the means to provide power capable of charging a mobile phone or powering a laptop, which it does via a handy USB socket. The predicted selling price for the purse when it hits the shelves is £150; thankfully it's large enough to hold about that amount! According to Hynek, he was looking for a design that would appeal to women 'interested in projecting power'. His goal, he says, is to 'use solar cells in a way that's unobtrusive to fashion while making something that's useful'. Hmm . . . useful it may be, but as for design, unobtrusive it's not. For his next venture he's turning to solar bracelets and ties.

Radioactive batteries

Researchers in the USA have developed a highly porous form of silicon that can be used to turn low levels of radiation efficiently into electricity. The silicon captures electrons emitted as the radioactive isotope tritium decays, producing useful electricity. So-called 'betabatteries' based on this principle would be very safe (Rolex watches already use tritium on the hands to make them glow in the dark), and would last for long periods of time (up to forty years), making them ideal for hard-to-reach applications such as sensors on remote bridges, weather monitoring stations and satellites.

Keeping junk food at arm's length

Cornell University Professor Brian Wansink urges would-be dieters to hide the sweetie jar, or at least move it more than two metres away. He and his researchers tempted forty university staff by placing a large jar of chocolates on their desks, either next to the staff member or two metres away. Every night the team counted how many treats had been consumed before restocking the jars. The results, although predictable, were striking. Hungry participants chomped their way through at least seven chocolates when the jars were right next to them, but only five when the jar was further away. And if an opaque jar was used in place of a clear-glass one, the rate of consumption fell by almost half – participants tucked into 4.5 and 3.1 chocolates on average when the coloured-glass jars were, respectively, next to them or two metres away. 'Not surprisingly,' Wansink points out, 'the less visible and less convenient the candy, the less people thought about it and were tempted.' So if you're like Oscar Wilde, who famously said, 'I can resist anything except temptation,' the moral of the story is: put the snacks in an opaque box, in a locked cupboard – and then throw away the key.

The pigeon-powered smog blog

Scientists have been turning to pigeons for help in understanding how urban pollution circulates and spreads. In 2006, Professor Beatriz da Costa from the University of California, Irvine, together with two students, Cina Hazegh and Kevin Ponto, announced that she was training twenty homing pigeons, each equipped with a smog-monitoring backpack, mobile phone and camera for release over San Jose, California. The idea is that the pigeons beam back text messages and photos detailing the pollution they encounter as they flutter to and fro, creating what is literally a bird's-eye view of the pollution problem.

In their announcement, the team explained that they had built a prototype system comprising a cellphone circuit-board and SIM card, a GPS receiver to pinpoint each of the birds' positions, and nitrogen dioxide and carbon monoxide sensors to monitor pollution. The next step is to shrink all of the components on to a single circuit-board to make a pigeon pollution pack for the birds to carry on their travels.

MEDICINE

Pacemakers for gorillas

In September 2004 a team of surgeons from the University of Alabama made veterinary medical history when they successfully inserted the first cardiac resynchronisation therapy (CRT) device into a gorilla at Birmingham Zoo. The recipient was Babec, the zoo's twenty-four-year-old western lowland gorilla, who had begun to show the symptoms of heart failure.

The CRT inserted into Babec is an advanced form of

pacemaker that allows both the right and left sides of the heart to be controlled independently. According to the zoo, he recovered well and quickly returned to some of his typical mannerisms – which presumably meant eating a lot of bananas and beating his chest. The device meant that Babec was able to enjoy an additional four years of good health before he died, in early 2008.

Can we clone spider silk?

Chemical synthesis is not economical. But scientists in Israel have artificially produced a form of spider silk which could be used commercially to make protective clothes such as bulletproof vests, surgical thread, optical fibres and even fishing rods. With researchers from Oxford and Munich, Uri Gat from the Hebrew University of Jerusalem isolated the genes that spiders use to make dragline silk, a form of web known for its strength and elasticity. By inserting these genes into cultured cells from a species of caterpillar, the researchers were able to make the cells assemble threads of the spider silk, which are six times stronger than similarly sized steel or nylon fibres.

Fatal fungus, the perfect anti-ant

A newly identified fungus discovered by scientists in the USA may provide the perfect Trojan horse for getting rid of ant and termite infestations without having to resort to pesticides or chemicals that are dangerous to humans and domestic animals. Previous attempts to use fungi to wipe out unwanted nests of ants and termites have failed because the ants normally stay well clear of fungi, apparently fully aware that fungal spores can prove lethal to their colonies. They even post guards to sniff out and bar from the nest individual ants that have been fungally infected while out foraging. But before it produces any such lethal spores, the newly discovered fungus secretes a substance which ants and termites find irresistible. They collect it and carry it back to the nest, and have even been known to turn it into a bed for the queen. Shortly afterwards, however, the fungus begins to produce spores, which infect and kill every member of the nest. Even better, once the nest has been wiped out, the smell of the residual spores deters reinfestation by fresh colonies of insects.

Paul Stamets, who made the discovery (in relation to carpenter ants in his home state of Washington) and has now set up a company to commercialise his green means of pest control, is currently screening different strains of the fungus to find any that are slower to begin spore production, which would provide sufficient time for nests to become sufficiently loaded with fungus to ensure the efficient and total destruction of the occupants.

Glowing fishing line highlights a weak spot

We've all heard the tale of the one that got away, but that might become a thing of the past if a new line in fishing tackle finds its way on to the market. Researchers Christoph Weder, Brent Crenshaw and Jill Kunzelman from Case Western Reserve University in Cleveland, Ohio, have come up with a new kind of line that changes colour when it reaches breaking point. It contains a polymer called phenylene vinylene oligomer which glows under ultraviolet light. Healthy line gives off a reddish-brown colour, whereas line that has been damaged by excessive tension, producing a weak spot, glows bright green instead. So just by waving an ultraviolet light over their tackle, anglers would be able to check that everything is in full working order (or not). Obviously UV light is not the most convenient way to examine the integrity of a long fishing line, so the next step will be to look for ways to produce a polymer with a colour change that is visible in normal light, too. Meanwhile, the team is also exploring how the material could be used as a tamper-proof cover – any damage to the polymer would show up as a green glowing patch.

 FACTOID:

'Arsenic is a deadly poison: the slightest amount in the human body is fatal.'

FALSE

Actually, the average person's body contains about ten milligrams of arsenic, and it is thought to stimulate the production of certain essential body substances. If animals are deprived of tiny levels of arsenic in their diet they will not grow properly. But large doses are indeed fatal.

MEDICINE

An illuminating way to track down veins

Doctors, paramedics – and vampires – could soon have yet another new tool at their disposal to help them find suitable veins for taking blood or inserting a drip. Biomedical scientist Herbert Zeman from the University of Tennessee in Memphis has unveiled a new device which uses near-infrared light to scan the skin for juicy veins. An image of what the camera sees is then projected back on to the patient's skin, producing a blood vessel 'road map' to guide doctors to the best sites for inserting a drip or collecting a blood sample. The machine illuminates the skin with an array of near-infrared LEDs, which are clustered around the camera and emit light at a wavelength of 740 nanometres. Light of this wavelength is strongly absorbed by blood but scattered and reflected by other tissues. So blood vessels look dark, whereas the surrounding tissues look much brighter. Set up correctly, the new device – about the size of a shoebox – can 'see' up to eight millimetres into the skin, and pinpoint the position of a vein with an accuracy of one-twentieth of a millimetre. It is likely to prove particularly useful for young children because their veins are often difficult to locate due to their small size and the presence of 'puppy fat'.

Less ringtone, more ringmoan

Looking to spice up the average mobile text life, in 2005 the adult-film company New Frontier Media branched out from ringtones and began to offer ring 'moans'. Fruity users will be able to download a selection of naughty noises said to range from the suggestive to the 'positively tantalising'.

Joined at the hip . . . or should that be molar?

Royal College of Art jewellery designer Nikki Stott has come up with a highly original concept in wedding bands – a ring grown from the bone of the betrothed. The rings are made with the help of Ian Thompson, a bioengineer at King's College, London. Bone-making cells are harvested from small pieces of the bone of each partner – such as slivers of jawbone collected when wisdom teeth are extracted. The bone cells, called osteoblasts, are then added to a culture dish where they take over a ring-shaped growth matrix which slowly dissolves as the cells colonise and begin to lay down new bone. When the process is complete, the resulting rough bone circles are then given to the designers who, in consultation with the couple, shape the bone into customised rings.

Electric bandage boosts wound-healing

Biomedical scientists in the USA have designed an electric bandage to help promote wound-healing. The new product is the brainchild of University of Alabama researcher Dale Feldman and is intended to help promote the healing of such injuries as pressure sores ('bedsores'), which are a common problem in patients immobilised by spinal injuries, strokes or old age. The bandage applies a tiny current across the wound site and has been shown to increase skin-injury-healing rates significantly in patients. Tests on rabbits have also shown that wounds close up 50 per cent more rapidly when the bandage is used. Electric fields have been used successfully in the past to stimulate tissue repair, and scientists have discovered more recently that, in skin wounds, electric currents naturally flow from the edges towards the base of the injury. New skin cells produced at the edges of the wound then follow this electrical gradient to find their way into the injury site and repair it.

FACTOID:

*'Many types of antifreeze are forms of
alcohol, yet the antidote for antifreeze
poisoning in a human is . . . more alcohol.'*

TRUE

One way to reverse the effects of methanol poisoning, and the glycol in antifreeze, is by administering
pure alcohol (ethanol): methanol, glycol and ethanol
are all metabolised by the same enzyme in your body,
so giving excess ethanol can stop the liver turning
the other alcohols into more harmful chemicals that
would otherwise damage the body.

MEDICINE

Are laptops linked to infertility?

A New York-based urologist has warned that laptops
actually used on a man's lap (as opposed to a table)
could be bad news for subsequent sperm counts. Dr
Yefim Sheynkin of Stony Brook Hospital studied twenty-
nine men in their twenties and thirties and found that
using a laptop on the lap for an hour increased the

temperature of the average scrotum by over 2.5° Celsius, potentially affecting fertility. Previous studies have found that raising scrotal temperature by as little as 1° Celsius is sufficient to affect sperm formation, but the volunteers in the laptop study achieved this rise in temperature after just fifteen minutes on the computer.

The effects of temperature on sperm formation are well known. A 1999 study showed that sperm production among American men can drop by over 40 per cent during the summer compared to the winter, and that in hotter temperatures sperm motility also drops and the number of defective sperms increases. On the basis of their findings, Sheynkin and his team argue that regular daily laptop use could lead to chronically low sperm counts, and they advise users to put their laptop on a table whenever possible. And uncross your legs too!

BIOTECHNOLOGY

Cows that make growth hormones in milk

Scientists from Buenos Aires in Argentina have created a genetically modified cow which pumps out human growth hormone in her milk. Called Pampa Mansa, the Jersey cow produces over four kilograms of the precious protein a year. She was created by adding the human gene for growth hormone to cow cells in a dish and then cloning a new cow from the modified cells. At her current rate of production, fifteen more animals like her would exceed the current world demand for this essential hormone, which is prescribed for patients with growth-hormone deficiency (of whom there are more than a thousand children needing regular doses in Argentina alone). Originally, patients were treated using hormone extracts obtained from pituitary glands taken from the brains of dead donors, but scares over transmitted diseases, including the degenerative brain disease CJD, have resulted in scientists switching to using genetically modified bacteria instead. Moreover, the traditional treatment remains very expensive, in Argentina costing a total of more than $US7 million annually. GM cows that are able to produce the protein in a readily purifiable form in their milk would provide a much cheaper alternative.

Spacecraft comet collision makes deep impact on observers

In July 2005, at a speed of 23,000 miles an hour (33,000 kilometres per hour), the 820-kilogram copper probe *Deep Impact* slammed into comet Tempel 1, opening up a football-field-sized crater on the surface of the 10-kilometre-long comet, and giving scientists a glimpse of the 4.5-billion-year-old material it contains. The collision was monitored from 450 kilometres away by an accompanying parent spacecraft equipped with cameras and spectrophotometers to analyse the composition of the comet.

Viewed as icy 'dirt-balls', most comets are essentially flying time capsules dating back billions of years to the time when the solar system was first formed. Locked inside are pristine samples of the elements and molecules that helped to form us, so blasting a comet apart produces a snapshot of the chemical composition of the early solar system.

During the previous year another probe, *Stardust*, had successfully retrieved samples from the stream of particles escaping from the surface of the comet Wild 2 (see page 180) and brought them back to Earth, where scientists are now analysing them. But what *Deep Impact* revealed when it smashed into Tempel 1 was that the comet's surface was much more powdery and less compacted than scientists had expected, and that although deposits of ice were detected, the quantity of ice was proportionately smaller than expected for the overall size of the comet body. So definitely more icy dirt-ball than the other way around.

FACTOID:

'The way people walk is so individual to them that it is possible to identify them solely by their gait.'

TRUE

Researchers at the Georgia Institute of Technology have found that the way you walk is almost as unique as your fingerprint. Indeed, early work on the project has shown that they can positively identify someone 80–95 per cent of the time just by looking at his or her walk. The system – which can use a normal camera but works best with radar – looks at a combination of movements, including the arms, legs and torso, and can identify people from up to 180 metres away.

TECHNOLOGY

Plastics with memory

German and American scientists have found out how to make plastics change shape when lights of specific wavelengths (in other words different colours) shine on them.

The 'programmed' materials can even return to their original shapes when exposed to light of a complementary wavelength. MIT engineer Robert Langer and his colleagues created the new 'shape memory' materials by adding light-sensitive molecules to the chemical composition of the plastic. This means that when an external stress is applied to the plastic at the same time as light of the correct colour, the photo-sensitive chemicals trigger the formation of a network of cross-links within the polymer, stabilising the new shape. The potential number of applications is huge, ranging from staples and paperclips that unlock at the flash of a torch, to tools for minimally invasive surgery such as blood-vessel stents that, on laser-light command, switch from slender threads to broad corkscrew shapes capable of holding open arteries.

MEDICINE

A robot you can wear

Rehabilitation after a stroke usually involves a course of repetitive muscle movements, but the intensity of the rehab makes it time- and labour-intensive. Now, biomedical engineer Jiping He and his colleagues at Arizona State University have developed a wearable robotic arm dubbed RUPERT – robotic upper extremity repetitive therapy – which aims to take some of the work out of the task. It uses pneumatic 'muscles' at the shoulder, elbow and wrist to recreate the right movements to aid recovery by helping to reinforce new nerve pathways that can be used to regain control of the muscle groups affected by the stroke.

What does your saliva say about your cancer risk?

Scientists at the University of California, Los Angeles, have developed a simple, non-invasive saliva test for mouth and throat cancers. The test picks up the products of genes that are normally switched off in healthy tissue but are inappropriately switched on in cancer cells, from which they spill into the saliva. The team, led by Dr David Wong, compared the saliva of thirty-two mouth-cancer patients with samples collected from healthy individuals of the same age; they were able to pinpoint four genes that were present in the saliva of cancer patients but absent from the mouths of healthy people. These four genes enabled them to pick up 91 per cent of the cancers in the study. Nevertheless, they still missed one cancer in ten, so they now plan to carry out a bigger trial to track down other genes which can also be used to make the test more accurate.

The benefit of this work is that head and neck cancers are often picked up late, by which time the tumour has already spread elsewhere in the body and is therefore much more difficult to treat effectively. A non-invasive saliva test could be used to pick up the condition much earlier, when it is considerably easier to treat and – hopefully – cure.

MEDICINE

We know a lot about countering HIV; surely it won't spread so easily again?

Doctors in the USA have described a patient with a highly aggressive multi-drug-resistant strain of HIV capable of triggering Aids just four months after infection. (Usually it takes ten to twenty years for this to happen.) Dr Martin Markowitz, from Rockefeller University in New York, found that the virus carried by the patient did not respond to any of the main anti-HIV drugs available. It appears that the man in question probably picked up several different strains of HIV in a short space of time, and these strains then exchanged genetic material among themselves to breed the highly aggressive and multi-resistant super-strain. The emergence of viruses like this is extremely worrying because it could spread to others.

MEDICINE

From blood cells to pancreatic cells

Scientists have come up with what could be a clever way to deal with diabetes – by persuading a class of white blood cells to turn into insulin factories. Juvenile-onset diabetes occurs when the immune system mistakenly wipes out the insulin-producing cells of the pancreas. Treating the disorder therefore relies on regularly replacing the missing insulin, which involves daily injections or, better still, replacing the lost insulin-secreting cells. With a view to doing the latter, German researcher Maren Ruhnke from University Hospital, Schleswig-Holstein, incubated blood cells called monocytes in a cocktail of pancreatic and immune-cell growth factors, which reprogrammed the monocytes to alter their appearance and behave instead like cells of the pancreas. When they were then transplanted into diabetic mice, the animals developed normal blood-sugar levels, suggesting that the same trick might work in humans.

Can chimps speak?

British researchers have discovered that chimpanzees make meaningful sounds to 'talk' to each other. Katie Slocombe from the University of St Andrews recorded the grunts produced by two chimps as they sampled bread and apples from two dispensers. She then played the recordings separately back to another chimp, who spent far more time fishing around the apple dispenser when he heard an 'apple' grunt, and more time poking in the bread dispenser when he heard a 'bread' grunt. The fact that this animal responded similarly to the grunts produced by two different chimps suggests that they are using referential communication.

Slocombe has since carried out similar experiments on wild chimpanzee groups in Uganda, which have shown that the animals can similarly discriminate between different types of 'scream' produced by members of their troop. For instance, they pay much more attention to screams elicited by an animal facing aggression from another individual than to the sound of one just having a tantrum. So not much different from a human in that respect then . . .

FACTOID:

'The latest mobile phone accessory is an airbag to protect the faces of users who have an accident during a call.'

FALSE

But Ericsson have invented a 'mobile-phone life jacket' so that people who take their phones on boats will find it harder to lose them overboard. The foam-filled buoyancy packs, which also contain a battery, snap on to the back of the phone in place of the standard battery. If the phone tumbles into the drink, it floats!

ECOLOGY

Researchers breathe easy after kerbside study

Surbjit Kaur and her colleagues at Imperial College have found that the closer you walk to the edge of the kerb, the greater your dose of airborne pollution. The researchers kitted out eleven volunteers with sampling devices that sucked in air as they took a twenty-minute stroll along London's busy Marylebone Road. When the team analysed the quantity of particulates trapped in the pumps' filters they found that individuals who had walked closest to the edge of the kerb had been exposed to 10 per cent more ultrafine particles than those walking further away, although the carbon monoxide dose was the same for both groups. Fine particles, particularly those produced by diesel engines, have been linked to respiratory problems, cancer and heart disease – so avoiding kerb-crawling seems to be the order of the day!

 FACTOID:

'The sex of a baby is determined by genes in the egg.'

FALSE

The sex of a baby is determined by the father's sperm, in which there may be either an X or Y chromosome. If the mother's egg – which carries only an X chromosome – is fertilised by a sperm carrying a Y, the result is a boy.

New therapy for allergy: a dose of worms

A team of researchers at Nottingham University, led by Professor David Pritchard, is investigating whether the immune-suppressing chemicals pumped out by intestinal hookworms to prevent them being expelled from the body can also damp down allergic conditions like asthma and hayfever.

The worms produce eggs that hatch into microscopic larvae that lie in wait on the ground until someone stands on them. Then, in a matter of minutes, they burrow through the skin and enter the bloodstream. The larvae first find their way to the lungs, where they each mature into an adult worm over a matter of weeks. They then crawl up to the throat and are swallowed, which carries them to their ideal home, the gut, where they latch on and feed on blood from the intestinal wall while also releasing eggs to continue the infectious cycle. To prevent the body rejecting its freeloading passenger, the worm also pumps out factors that cause the immune system to ignore it. One possible side-effect of this might be that symptoms of an overactive immune system, such as allergies, could be alleviated. To find out, the Nottingham team has been conducting clinical trials on patients with asthma whom they have infected with ten hookworms each. So far, the worms have been well tolerated by the patients, but the researchers have found only a small difference in the reactivity of the patients' airways. This, they say, indicates that better tests are necessary, including more accurate mimicking of the way in which the infection occurs naturally, since in parts of the world where parasites like hookworms are common, allergy rates are very low.

Blinding insects to smells

Scientists have unearthed the genetic mechanism that enables insects to pick up smells. Without it they cannot detect airborne odours, including that of their next meal. Researchers hope this dicovery will lead to the development of powerful new insect repellents capable of making humans and crops 'invisible' to mosquitoes and other pests. Leslie Vosshall and colleagues from Rockefeller University have found that insects – including mosquitoes, plant pests like the corn earworm moth (which damages corn, tomato and cotton crops) and fruit flies, which home in on rotting fruit – all rely on the same gene, known as Or83b, to detect smells. When the researchers removed the gene from laboratory fruit flies, the insects essentially lost their sense of smell. To find out why, the team looked more closely at the insects' antennae – their equivalent of a nose – and found that all of the receptors (chemical docking stations) that enable nerve cells to pick up the presence of an odour were missing. But they returned when the scientists replaced the absent Or83b gene, even if it was the equivalent gene taken from an insect of a different species. The Or83b gene therefore seems to play a key role in ensuring that smell receptors find their way to the correct places on the nerve cells in insect antennae, and might prove to be an Achilles heel that can be exploited for the development of novel insect repellents which work by blocking insects' sense of smell. According to Vosshall, 'If we could use this to interrupt the transport of odorant receptors, we could make mosquitoes "blind" to humans. That, in turn, would be a good way to prevent disease transmission.'

The heart-powered robot

Researchers in California have developed a self-assembling nanobot (a miniature robot) that 'walks' along powered by heart-muscle cells. Jianzhong Xi and colleagues made the tiny micro-machine – which measures just over a tenth of a millimetre and takes steps three-hundredths of a millimetre long – by adding heart-muscle cells to a 'backbone' made from a wafer of silicon shaped like a flattened U. Before the muscle cells are added, a polymer layer and then a gold film are first laid down in a specific pattern on top of the silicon. Muscle cells attach well to gold, but not to the polymer, so the pattern of the two can be used to dictate where the cells can latch on. Guided by this pattern, the muscle cells link themselves across the open 'legs' of the U-shaped backbone. Because they have a built-in pacemaker, heart-muscle cells automatically contract and relax, opening and closing the 'legs' of the robot and enabling it to walk.

The researchers suggest that in the future, as well as walking around, devices like this could be rigged up as tiny implantable generators that run on glucose picked up from the bloodstream and use piezoelectric materials to power microelectronic circuitry – in other words, the robot's future 'brain' – or other implantable electronic devices.

FACTOID:

*'H. S. Richardson, son of the inventor of
Vick's VapoRub™, the cold remedy, in 1907
renamed the product after his brother-in-law,
Victor Richardson.'*

FALSE

He named it after his brother-in-law Joshua Vick.
(A man very rarely has the same surname as his
brother-in-law.) But it was undoubtedly an
improvement on 'Richardson's Croup and Pneumonia Cure Salve' and remains popular all over the
world. In Britain alone, 2.5 million jars of 'Vick'
menthol ointment are sold every year.

SPACE SCIENCE

The price of meteorites? Sky-high!

Meteorites are the latest fashionable must-have, it
seems. Some private collectors are willing to shell out
up to $6000 per gram – that's three hundred times
the price of the equivalent weight in gold – to own one.
The surging price is fuelling the meteorite equivalent of

a gold rush as prospectors head for locations such as the remote Sahara and Gobi deserts and Patagonia, where the arid conditions preserve specimens for millions of years. The unfortunate spin-off is that scientists are getting priced out of the market, which means that precious specimens dating from the birth of our solar system, or the early history of Mars, are being lost to research and instead ending up on people's mantelpieces. To combat the problem, scientists at the University of Arizona, armed with $200,000, have set up the Southwest Meteorite Center to buy up samples before they disappear into private collections. They will also analyse and authenticate meteorites for collectors in return for a small sample. The specimens they accumulate will be stored in a climate-controlled facility to prevent further chemical deterioration, and made available to other scientists on request.

TECHNOLOGY

The next generation of computer chips is not such a PC of cake to make

For many years the computer industry has been following the rule of Moore's Law – which states that the number of transistors (microcircuits) on a chip doubles roughly every eighteen months, and hence so does the processing power. This is because more components can be crammed on to a chip and the distance between them reduced, which cuts down the delays as they communicate with each other. But technology is beginning to push the boundaries of what silicon-based chips can achieve, because the components are becoming so small that they will soon interfere with each other quantum-mechanically. To solve the problem, researchers are instead attempting to borrow from biology, which is extremely good at arranging tiny molecules in very small spaces. This means that materials like DNA and proteins, which can have a pre-programmed structure, are now being used to position nano-particle chip components accurately, potentially shrinking processing to the scale of individual molecules and greatly increasing the speed and power of computing.

BACTERIA

Bacterial sonar

Scientists have found that bacteria use a sonar-like system to spot other cells around themselves in order to target them for destruction. This finding explains how some bacteria seem to 'know' when to switch on the production of certain toxins designed to break open nearby cells, including other micro-organisms. This can help to release useful nutrients, to help the bug spread and to ward off attack from the immune system.

Working on an intestinal bug called *Enterococcus*, Michael Gilmore and his team at Harvard have found that the bacterium releases two chemicals into its surroundings. One of the two substances sticks on to foreign cells, while the second substance reports back to the bug, telling it to make the toxin. But if there are no cells near by, the first substance sticks to the second and prevents it from reporting back, and so no toxins are made. The scientists say that the discovery will help to design new treatments to combat bacterial infections by designing toxin inhibitors, which will be particularly useful for tackling antibiotic-resistant bugs. The researchers also hope that it might be possible to 'tame' certain bacteria and engineer the system so that it can be used to detect other things in the environment, such as minerals, or other disease-causing bugs.

Burglars caught by appetite for crime

Inviting colleagues to a free buffet, DNA fingerprint expert Heather Zarsky had an ulterior motive. She asked diners to sample a range of foods, leaving what they didn't want. From the leftovers she extracted complete DNA profiles of nearly half the diners, and partial profiles from a further third. The aim of the experiment was to work out what foodstuffs preserve the best evidence of the antics of peckish burglars. Apparently, hungry housebreakers often can't resist raiding the fridge, but frequently abandon their spoils half eaten, providing the police with valuable clues to the identity of the perpetrator – but only if they know what foods to home in on. Now they do: apples, cheese, carrots and pizza. Would-be burglars are therefore advised to eschew these items in favour of chocolate, which proved useless at identifying a snacker.

 FACTOID:

'A jug of hot water placed in the freezer turns to ice more quickly than an identical jug of cold water.'

FALSE

Hot water will always take longer to freeze than water that starts cold. But it *is* true that the hot water will begin by losing proportionately more heat more quickly, a fact that has led to this common assumption.

What makes animals hibernate?

Japanese researchers have uncovered the chemical switch that controls an animal's hibernation pattern, a finding that might hold the key to triggering similar states of suspended animation in humans. To discover the hibernation trigger, Noriaki Kondo and colleagues at the Mitsubishi Kagaku Institute of Life Sciences in Tokyo studied a large group of chipmunks. They found that the levels of a hormone in the blood called hibernation-specific protein (HP) changed in accordance with when the animals hibernated, and showed an annual cyclical change in levels. HP dropped just before the animals went to sleep, and remained low throughout their hibernation. When they woke up, the levels rose again. But in their cerebrospinal fluid, which surrounds the brain, the opposite was true: when the animals went to sleep, HP levels rose. To confirm that HP was responsible, the researchers used an antibody to mop up the molecule in the brain which, as predicted, prevented the animals from nodding off. Now they need to find out exactly how the hormone works, and whether the same effects might be possible in humans. After all, if humans can be put into a similar state, it might be possible to reduce tissue damage caused by strokes, heart attacks and surgery by simulating the extremely low metabolic demands of hibernating tissues.

FACTOID:

'Because bones have to be strong, they must also be heavy – they account for at least one-quarter of the body's total weight.'

FALSE

They account for just over one-eighth– about 14 per cent – and a little more in men than in women.

CHEMISTRY

Wet washing spin-off

Two US researchers have discovered a chemical trick to wring the last drips out of wet washing. Dinesh Shah and Daniel Carter at the University of Florida have found that clothes remain wet after a wash (even with a spin cycle thrown in) because the tiny gaps between the strands of a fabric act like capillary tubes, tightly holding on to water by surface tension. But by researching a detergent-and-softener cocktail that locks on to the fabric and breaks down water surface tension, the two scientists have been able to persuade even the most stubborn fabrics to shed 20 per cent more water during the spin cycle than they would normally, meaning that the clothes are helping to dry themselves 20 per cent more quickly – using less energy in the process.

Parental smoking hooks kids

Research suggests that passive smoking can 'prime' a child's brain for nicotine, making it more prone to addiction later. Margaret Becklake from McGill University in Montreal recruited almost two hundred nine-year-old boys and girls, testing their lung capacities and their saliva for nicotine breakdown products, and logging their parents' smoking habits. Four years later she followed up with the same children. Those who had had the highest levels of nicotine breakdown products in their saliva (indicating greater exposure to passive smoking) were twice as likely to have become smokers by the age of thirteen.

A gut instinct for allergies

Scientists have found further evidence that friendly bacteria in the intestine play an important role in preventing allergic conditions, including asthma. Killing them off with antibiotics, they say, might be partly responsible for the surge in allergies over the last twenty years.

So how can bacteria down in the stomach and intestines affect the sensitivity of the airways elsewhere in the body? Because anything that is breathed in ultimately ends up being swallowed: mucus produced in the lungs traps inhaled particles and is then wafted up to the throat, from where the particles proceed down into the stomach. In the intestines the immune system learns to recognise whether a substance is dangerous or not, and to ignore or tolerate harmless substances. The success of this process depends upon the micro-organisms (known as the flora) that inhabit the intestines. If the balance of gut micro-organisms is upset by antibiotics, a change of diet, or switching from breast milk to formula, then the tolerance process can break down, triggering allergies.

University of Michigan researcher Gary Huffnagle has found, in experimental animals, that exposure to certain allergens, including mould spores or pollens, at the same time as the body's gut flora are altered can result in the development of an allergy to that substance. His suggestion? Try to eat a healthy diet packed with fruit and vegetables, especially after a course of antibiotics, to help maintain a thriving population of the right sort of intestinal micro-organisms.

Horses left- or right-'handed'? You're talking fetlocks!

Knowing whether a horse is right- or left-'handed' might help you to beat the bookies in future, according to researchers from the University of Limerick. Riders and trainers often report that their mounts respond better when turning or jumping in one direction or the other, but whether this is down to training or to an underlying innate cause has until now remained unknown. To find out, Jack Murphy and his team studied forty untrained horses destined to become show-jumpers or dressage competitors. They watched which leg the animals preferred to use when stepping forward, and which direction they chose when detouring around obstacles or rolling over on the floor. The researchers found that females preferred the right side, whereas male horses preferred their left. About 10 per cent of all horses showed no preference. Because a well-balanced mount is the most desirable for riding and racing, these results could help trainers and jockeys to develop their mounts' weak sides. Meanwhile, however, knowing a horse's preferred side could help punters predict the horse's competition performance, because the direction and bends in a race will evidently suit some runners better than others. Bad news for the bookies!

FACTOID:

'Beards are bad for your health.'

TRUE

Men who shave regularly are healthier and have sex more often than their hairier counterparts, a study has shown. Researchers at the University of Bristol found that men who shave at least once a day are more likely to be married, have better jobs and are less likely to smoke, whereas bearded men in addition have a 70 per cent higher chance of suffering a stroke.

Can you predict dementia?

A new study has shown that measuring people's brain waves might hold the key to predicting who is at risk of developing dementia over the next ten years. US researchers Leslie Prichep and Roy John from the New York University Medical School monitored a group of forty-four men and women who were aged between sixty-four and seventy-nine and had normal brain function at the time they joined the study. On several occasions over the following seven to ten years the volunteers had their brain waves measured non-invasively using a technique known as an electroencephalogram (EEG). By the end of the study, twenty-seven of the patients had developed signs of dementia. By looking back at the earlier brain-wave measurements of these subjects, the researchers were able to pinpoint characteristic changes in brain activity which occurred before the patients developed outward signs of cognitive decline. In particular, the researchers noted, there was an increase in a pattern of brain activity known as theta waves, and a loss of synchronisation between the brain's two cerebral hemispheres. These results suggest that it might be possible to use this technique to screen for individuals at risk of dementia.

Lies are clearly unpalatable

Forget polygraph tests to flush out a liar; criminals could soon be given away by their stomachs, according to research carried out at the University of Texas by Pankaj Pasricha and his colleagues. The team gave sixteen volunteers an electrogastrogram, a measurement of the nerve activity in the stomach. The subjects were asked to lie about some things, and tell the truth about others. Intriguingly, their stomach nerve activity shot up whenever they told a lie but remained unchanged when they were honest – evidence, says Pasricha, 'that the gut has a mind of its own'.

Handbag interior illumination, anyone?

Anyone who has spent ages rummaging around in a handbag for her keys on a dark evening, usually in the rain, will appreciate a new self-illuminating solar-powered handbag designed by Brunel University's Rosanna Kilfedder. Dubbed the Sun Trap, the bag is powered by an internal battery. Whenever the zip is opened, the electroluminescent lining glows, showing you what's inside. It switches off again automatically after fifteen seconds to prevent the battery going flat if the bag is left open by accident. As an added bonus, on sunny days an array of external solar panels can help to recharge the battery, which can also be used to run a mobile phone, or even an MP3 player. Bag me one, please . . .

BIOLOGY

Frogs croak in ultrasound

US researcher Albert Feng and his colleagues have found that a species of Chinese frog that lives in a noisy environment has evolved a clever way to prevent its mating calls being drowned out by the sound of nearby running water – it croaks in ultrasound. The researchers discovered by accident the strange vocal habits of the male concave-eared torrent frog (*Amolops tormotus*), which lives in a mountainous region of China, while using sensitive recording equipment to monitor the frogs' activity. As well as croaking the conventional way, the team found, these frogs were producing very high-pitched noises (up to thirty-four kilohertz), inaudible to humans. When the researchers recorded the sounds and played them back to captive (male) frogs, they learned that their study subjects croaked in unison with the recording.

To find out how the frogs were responding to the ultrasound, the researchers then temporarily blocked up the animals' ears, instantly stopping the karaoke. Feng and his team believe that the sounds are a mating call designed to cut through the loud noises of running water that are prevalent in the frogs' aquatic environment. They are now eager to track down some females to see how (or, indeed, if) they respond to an ultrasonic 'ribbit'.

The robot that really gets under your skin

Scientists at the University of Nebraska Medical Center in Omaha have developed a tiny robotic surgeon which can wander around inside the body, providing doctors with a minimally invasive look at what they need to see, or performing minor surgical or biopsy tasks. Dmitry Oleynikov and his team's tiny device, which is only fifteen millimetres across, consists of two rotating aluminium cylinders linked by a thick axle that also carries a camera. A spiral tread pattern on the cylinders enables them to grip the walls of the abdominal cavity to move around, and the robot itself is controlled by an external joystick held by the surgeon.

So far, the team has used the robot to assist in removing a pig's gall bladder, and has explored the abdomen of a live pig, driving the robot down the animal's interior through a small incision in the stomach wall. The benefit, of course, is that such an intervention requires no other, larger, external incisions, so avoiding unsightly scars. In addition, more than one robot can be passed through the same small incision to provide different angles of vision for the controlling surgeons.

MEDICINE

A gene for sydelxia?

Jeffrey Gruen and his team from Yale University have pinpointed a gene that causes dyslexia. The researchers screened the genes of 536 subjects from 153 families with a history of dyslexia, enabling them to home in on a region of chromosome 6, where they found that a piece of DNA was missing. The affected gene, DCDC2, is normally switched on in parts of the brain that are involved in reading and language-processing. Presumably, in people carrying the defective gene, some nerve cells fail to migrate to the correct position during the brain's development.

GENETICS

Genome of man's best friend

US scientists have decoded the dog genome sequence. According to Eric Lander and his colleagues from MIT, since dogs exhibit an enormous range of physical and behavioural traits – in particular, susceptibility to certain diseases – the genome sequence will enable researchers to pinpoint the genetic bases of these traits. And because humans suffer many of the same diseases as dogs, tracking down the combinations of genes that make dogs sick will also highlight the causes in humans. So once again dogs have proved that they are man's best friend.

TECHNOLOGY

Tide of enthusiasm for wave-power invention

A UK-based engineer, Ed Spooner, has come up with a more efficient way to generate electricity from wave power. His solution is a clever, seabed-mounted device, dubbed 'the snapper', which turns the ponderous movement of ocean swells into a succession of rapid movements ideal for electricity production.

The snapper comprises a floating buoy tethered to a mobile central armature within the generator on the seabed. As the buoy rises and falls on passing waves it draws the armature, containing a series of fixed magnets, up and down past a series of coils in the base unit. This movement induces pulses of electrical current in the wire. But to produce the rapid movements required to generate electricity efficiently, a second set of fixed magnets in the base unit, aligned with the magnets on the armature, holds the armature in place until the rising buoy generates enough upward thrust to pull the magnets apart and allow the armature to move up to the next set of magnets, which are placed vertically above the first. As the buoy continues to rise this action is repeated several times. When the armature reaches the top of its travel, and the buoy begins to fall down the wave, a spring returns the armature to the starting position, again as a series of short, sharp movements.

This process turns what would otherwise be a gentle up-and-down motion into a succession of swift, electricity-generating jerks. A prototype of the invention shows that the system produces increased current-generating forces compared with existing technologies and might therefore enable wave-power systems to be made smaller, cheaper and more efficient.

One flew over the cuckoo's nest . . .

Researchers have come to understand how the African village weaverbird (*Ploceus cucullatus*) prevents itself being taken for a ride by cuckoos: it's all down to the speckles on the eggs. David Lahti and his colleagues at the University of Massachusetts have described how village weaverbirds lay clutches of eggs which all show a very similar pattern of speckles, suggesting that if a cuckoo laid an egg in the nest, the weaverbird will be able to spot the impostor almost immediately. When the researchers studied two colonies of the birds that had been introduced more than two hundred years ago to two islands without any cuckoos, they found that those birds' eggs no longer exhibited the speckle patterns. In a neat demonstration of the power of evolution, these results show how, in the absence of pressure from parasitic cuckoos, the appearance of the eggs has altered because having a distinctive pattern is no longer so much of an advantage.

FACTOID:

'It is a scientific fact that a facility for story-telling may be inherited.'

TRUE

A substance found in the brain and known by the abbreviation BDNF has two variant forms called 'met' and 'val'; one of its main functions has to do with long-term memory. People with the val form are better at recalling stories, whereas those with the met form are more susceptible to the effects of ageing, depression and Alzheimer's.

MEDICINE

Stem cells get to the heart of cardiac repair

Scientists at Johns Hopkins University in Baltimore, Maryland, have announced that stem-cell therapy can be used effectively to treat heart damage caused by heart attacks (known as myocardial infarcts) in pigs, paving the way for using the same technique in humans. The scientists injected each pig with about two hundred million mesenchymal stem cells collected from the bone marrow of other adult pigs. The injections, which covered an area of the heart wall about the size of a small coin, were placed directly into a region of heart muscle recently damaged by an infarct, by threading a small catheter into the heart via an artery. A second 'control' group of pigs received placebo injections lacking any stem cells. The pigs were then monitored for two months. The pigs that received placebo injections became much worse and developed congestive heart failure. But those that had received the stem-cell injections showed full recovery of heart function and their hearts contained virtually no signs of 'scarring', a cardinal signature of previous heart attacks. In such scars muscle tissue is replaced by stiff fibrous tissue which cannot contract properly, reducing the heart's pumping ability, and the scar itself can also affect the electrical properties of the heart, sometimes triggering rhythm disturbances and cardiac arrest.

Pigs provide a useful comparison with humans because their organs and physiology are very similar to our own. These encouraging findings suggest that this technique may work effectively in humans.

How urgent is this message?

A voicemail system developed by scientists at MIT can label messages as urgent, not urgent, formal, informal, happy, sad, excited or calm, just by analysing the caller's tone of voice. Named Emotive Alert, the system, designed by Zeynep Inanoglu and Ron Caneel, studies the volume, pitch and speed of the first ten seconds of each message and compares the results with eight stored 'acoustic fingerprints' representative of the eight message types. The system then labels the message accordingly and sends the recipient a text message emoticon corresponding to the message type. The acoustic fingerprints were produced by feeding hundreds of voice messages, which had been grouped into each of the different categories, into a computer learning package to pick out the features they all had in common.

In tests so far the system can tell happy from sad and excited from calm, but it finds formal versus informal and urgent versus non-urgent more difficult to tell apart. This is probably because formality and urgency tend to be conveyed more in the wording, which the machine does not analyse, rather than the sound, which it does.

Frozen 'fossil bacteria' brought back to life

NASA scientists working on samples of Alaskan permafrost have discovered a form of life that has been frozen in time for over thirty thousand years. When the scientists thawed the ice under a microscope the newly identified organisms, bacteria now called *Carnobacterium pleistocenium*, showed signs of life and began swimming around. They date back to an era when mammoths and sabre-toothed tigers roamed the Earth, and were collected from a tunnel drilled through the ice near the town of Fox.

Richard Hoover, who made the discovery, says that the findings raise the prospect of finding life on Mars, because the bacteria were extracted from half-metre-thick wedges of ice similar to structures seen on the red planet. Indeed, the *Mars Express* probe has revealed the presence of a giant frozen sea near the Martian equator, which could provide ideal conditions for microbial activity.

FACTOID:

'The symptoms of the common cold are caused always and only by virus infection, so antibiotics do not help at all.'

FALSE

Virus infection certainly causes the vast majority of colds, but some of the symptoms in some cases may be produced by secondary infection by bacterial agents – in which case, antibiotics can help – or by allergic sensitivity, or even by a dramatic change in environmental temperature or air quality.

TECHNOLOGY

DNA nano-scale origami

A US researcher has found a way to perform the DNA equivalent of origami, paving the way for the construction of complex nano-scale structures, including the next generation of microchips. Paul Rothemund from the California Institute of Technology uses a piece of single-stranded DNA made up of seven thousand DNA 'letters' which he folds, rather like a piece of modelling wire, using additional short pieces of DNA called oligo-nucleotides. These oligonucleotides lock on to a unique 'address' on the DNA strand, and when they bind they staple the DNA into the correct shape. Linking other nano-particles to the oligonucleotides, like a molecular cargo, allows researchers to position more molecules with great precision, including potentially the components required to assemble nano-scale circuits and computer chips. This is a key area of exploration by the microprocessor industry, which, within the next ten years, faces 'red wall' – a point at which, using present techniques, it will become impossible to make computer chips any more powerful (see also page 212).

Nature versus nurture

Researchers from Switzerland and the USA have found that puberty plays a big role in the songs sung by canaries. Rockefeller University researcher Tim Gardner and his colleagues found that canaries will quite happily learn the 'wrong song' if it's played to them when they are young. But as soon as the birds hit the avian equivalent of puberty and receive an adolescent burst of testosterone, they appear immediately to unlearn all the incorrect lessons they've been taught and instead revert to a singing style much more characteristic of their species. According to the researchers, 'At sexual maturity, when the song would be important for courting females, rules interfered.' In other words, just like human teenagers dumping the Spiderman duvet cover, canaries change their tune when it comes to the opposite sex.

Jumping genes make the brain unique

Among all the myriad genes in the genome are 'mobile elements' corresponding to pieces of DNA that may 'jump' into the middle of other genes, altering their activity. Now scientists at the Salk Institute in California have shown that this process takes place in the developing brain, where it affects what sorts of cells are produced as the nervous system develops. According to Alysson Muotri, who made the discovery by tracking the behaviour of one such 'jumping genetic element' called L1, this could explain why identical twins, despite sharing the same genetic material, don't always develop the same neurological diseases such as Alzheimer's or schizophrenia. The degree of randomness contributed by these mobile elements to the way the brain develops helps to drive neural diversity, ensuring that each person really is 'an individual', and perhaps explains some aspects of the power of the human mind.

Worms can combat Crohn's

Researchers have stumbled upon a possible new treatment for the inflammatory intestinal condition Crohn's disease – a dose of worms! The immune systems of patients with Crohn's are thought to be overreacting to the 'good' bacteria in the intestine, producing painful and recurrent inflammation, ulceration, weight loss and intestinal obstruction. The disease tends to be much more common in the developed world than in the Third World, where most people carry intestinal parasites such as worms, and this has led doctors to speculate that worms in some way help to damp down the immune response in the gut. So, over a six-month period, University of Iowa researcher Robert Summers and his colleagues gave twenty-nine volunteers with Crohn's disease regular doses of the eggs of a species of worm called *Trichuris suis*, which normally infects pigs. After twelve weeks of worm therapy, nineteen of the patients were completely free of Crohn's symptoms. By the end of the study, 80 per cent of the patients had responded to the therapy, and 73 per cent had gone into remission and were symptom-free. No one in the study developed any side-effects.

The benefit of using pig worms is that, once they hatch, the worms remain in the bowel without invading other parts of the body, and the eggs do not pose a threat to other people because they must be incubated in soil for at least a week before they can colonise another person. The authors suggest that the worms are producing factors that help to suppress the overactivity of the immune system in the bowel, and that worm therapy might be a simple alternative, or even addition, to Crohn's therapy in future. Elsewhere in the world, scientists are trying the same trick to combat other immune problems, including allergies and asthma (see page 207), and clinical trials are currently in progress.

FOOD

I could eat the whole menu – literally

Most people expect just to look at the menu in a restaurant, but thanks to chef Homaru Cantu, owner of restaurant Moto, now you can taste it too. That's because he has come up with a concoction of vegetable dyes that can be used to replace the ink in an ink-jet printer. Replace the paper with soybean or starch sheets and you have, quite literally, an edible menu. As the sheets roll off the printer Cantu covers them with a mixture of flavourings and then fries, freezes or bakes the results, creating 'dishes' of a very different kind! Diners at his restaurant are also invited to spice up their food by tearing strips off the menu and adding them to their meal. The new invention ushers in the possibility of edible adverts in magazines or newspapers, where readers will be able to try a new flavour of crisp or a new type of pizza before they buy.

And the magic doesn't end there. Cantu also has plans to cook steak, and even bread, 'inside-out' using a laser, producing steaks that are seared in the centre but raw on the outside, and loaves that are crusty in the middle! So it may not be long before you can go into a restaurant and order something you like the lick of . . .

MEDICINE

Schizophrenia is heralded by confusion in the identification of smells

Researchers in Australia have found that your nose – or rather, its ability to identify certain smells correctly – could hold the key to detecting people who are at risk of mental illness. We've known for some time that people with schizophrenia are unable to recognise smells correctly – they might identify the smell of pizza as 'orange', or bubblegum as 'smoke'. But no one knew what came first – whether the schizophrenia was subsequently causing the difficulty in identifying smells, or the same neurological trait that triggers schizophrenia also affects olfaction. By studying a group of people who were at high risk of developing mental illness, Warrick Brewer and Christos Pantelis from the University of Melbourne found that all of the patients who went on to develop schizophrenia displayed the inability to identify smells correctly *before* they showed any other symptoms of schizophrenia. 'An accurate and reliable diagnostic tool for schizophrenia could allow for early treatment or prevention and minimise the extensive and significant distress to those in the community directly and indirectly affected,' says Brewer.

 FACTOID:

'Camels' humps can hold up to fifteen litres of water.'

FALSE

Camels' humps don't hold *any* water – they store fat, which they can use to sustain themselves when food is scarce. Incredibly, these amazing desert-adapted animals can actually go without any water or food for over a week if they need to.

Stiff upper lip

Researchers in New York have found that rather than just losing their natural elasticity as we get older, skin cells actually become more rigid, contributing to the ageing effect. Clarkson University scientist Tamara K. Berdyyeva and her colleagues used tissue-culture techniques to grow human skin cells obtained from the foreskins of recently circumcised baby boys. As the cells 'aged' by dividing in the dish, the researchers made measurements of their 'stiffness'. Old cells, they found, were significantly stiffer than their younger counterparts. The reason, say the researchers, is because the cytoskeleton, the 'scaffolding' that holds the cells together, becomes more rigid in older cells. But the good news is that there are drugs that can weaken the cytoskeleton, which might therefore make excellent anti-wrinkle creams and which the research team is now testing.

Olive oil is as good as ibuprofen

Researcher Paul Breslin and his colleagues from the Monell Chemical Senses Center and the Universities of

Pennsylvania and Philadelphia have found that, at least when it comes to pain relief, top-of-the-range olive oil is as good as a dose of ibuprofen, possibly explaining the beneficial effects of the so-called Mediterranean diet. The team tracked down a component of the oil called oleocanthal which, like ibuprofen, blocks the action of the enzyme cyclooxygenase, involved in inflammation. About fifty millilitres (three tablespoons) of olive oil is equivalent to a standard dose of aspirin, which may explain why people who eat an olive-oil-rich diet traditionally have lower levels of heart disease and stroke. Olive oil also tastes nice, which is another bonus!

Petrified wood perfect for a catalytic converter

US researchers have found a way to achieve in days what takes nature millions of years – creating petrified wood, which, say the inventors, could hold the key to more efficient industrial catalysts, filters and materials for cleaning up spills and pollutants. That's because petrified wood is very hard but also very porous, with a large internal surface area, making it ideal for soaking up or separating substances, or acting as a catalytic converter. Wood naturally becomes petrified (turned to stone) when it is buried in an oxygen-poor soil that prevents it from breaking down. Slowly, over millions of years, the organic material is replaced by minerals, such as silicates, which are soaked up from the surrounding soil. To speed up the process, the research team from the Pacific North-west National Laboratory took blocks of wood, gave them an acid bath and then soaked them in a silica solution for a few days to saturate the wood with minerals. They then baked the wood at 1400° Celsius in an argon furnace designed to exclude oxygen. The result was a new silicon carbide, which, according to scientist Yongsoon Shin, exactly replicates petrified wood. The researchers have now focused their efforts on trying to produce narrower, highly ordered pores in the new silicon carbide in order to boost its industrial potential.

MEDICINE

Why does booze make us drunk?

Alcohol has been used by humans for medicinal and recreational purposes for thousands of years, but scientists still aren't sure how it makes us tipsy. To tackle the problem, researchers in the USA studied a family of rats that have a tendency to be highly sensitive to the effects of alcohol. These rats carry an altered version of a gene used by brain cells to respond to the brain's main inhibitory nerve transmitter chemical, GABA (gamma-aminobutyric acid). The researchers tested the electrical activity of the rats' brains and found that giving them alcohol made their nerve cells much more sensitive to the inhibitory (depressant) effects of GABA compared with normal rats, possibly explaining why alcohol makes people sleepy, lethargic and uncoordinated. When the rats were given behavioural tests after drinking small amounts of alcohol (producing a blood-alcohol level below the drink-drive limit in most countries) they became very uncoordinated, compared with normal rats given the same amount to drink. These results suggest that alcohol produces its intoxicating effects by interfering with the brain's inhibitory neuro-transmitter systems. They might help to identify individuals who are at risk of alcohol-related problems, and might also contribute to strategies to reverse drunkenness.

ZOOLOGY

How do ants tell friend from foe?

Biologists have known for some time that all of the ants from a single nest exude an identical cocktail of volatile substances called cuticular hydrocarbons, enabling them to recognise each other. But how their antennae facilitated that recognition was something of a mystery. Now, Japanese researcher Mamiko Ozaki from the Kyoto Institute of Technology has pinpointed a specialised sensory structure located on the antennae, called a sensillum, which sounds the alert when things don't smell right.

The sensillum is a tiny tube about 0.02 millimetres long and about 0.004 millimetres in diameter, which houses a large number (up to two hundred) of chemically sensitive nerve fibres. By painstakingly recording the activity in the nerve fibres from the sensillum, Ozaki found that they fired off nerve impulses only when he exposed them to smells of 'foreign' (non-nest-mate) ants. Cleverly, the nerves that would normally respond to the smells of nest-mates were deactivated, sorting friend from foe.

 FACTOID:

'The average person's brain weighs five hundred grams (just over a pound).'

FALSE

The human brain weighs up to three times that amount – between 1.2 and 1.5 kilograms (2¼ and 3 pounds) – with men's brains generally slightly heavier than women's.

Asteroid to pass Earth inside the moon's orbit

Space enthusiasts will be treated to our closest encounter yet with a passing asteroid, which will be visible from the ground as it buzzes Earth, passing inside the orbit of some of our satellites. Scientists first spotted the three-hundred-metre-wide near-Earth object, which they called 2004 MN4, hurtling towards us in June 2004. Initially, it was thought to be on a collision course with us, but subsequent observations – specifically, measurements taken in December 2004 – have enabled scientists to refine the course and eliminate the possibility of a direct impact with either us or the moon. Instead, they think it will pass us by at a distance of 36,350 kilometres from the Earth's centre, just below the altitude of our geostationary satellites, and will be visible to the naked eye to people in Europe, Africa and western Asia, appearing as a fast-moving star passing through the constellation of Cancer. Slightly worryingly, it is due to arrive on Friday, the 13 April 2029.

So what if it does hit us? Scientists are confident that if an asteroid of this size collided with Earth, it would cause local devastation and regional damage, but wouldn't generate any sort of global disruption. Which is reassuring, given that 2004 MN4 (more technically known now as 99942 Apophis) is due to return in 2036, and again in 2069.

Venus flytrap caught on camera

Charles Darwin called the Venus flytrap (*Dionaea muscipula*) one of the most wonderful things in the world – yet more than 150 years later researchers are still struggling to explain how the plant closes its trap so quickly. Previously, scientists had suggested that the rapid closure occurs when special 'motor cells' deflate, rather like a balloon popping, which brings the two halves of the leaf together. But even this would not account for the speed with which the process takes place. To solve the problem, Yoel Forterre from the Centre National de la Recherche Scientifique in France, together with colleagues in the USA and the UK, used high-speed photography, capable of capturing four hundred frames a second, to track what happens during the tenth of a second the trap takes to close. The photos have revealed that the flytrap 'snaps' from a convex shape to a concave shape very quickly, just like a broken tennis ball turned inside-out that can rapidly be 'popped' from one stable shape to another. This is achieved by the arrangement of cells and fibres within the wall of the leaf – although the scientists haven't yet worked out precisely how the arrival of a potential meal inside the trap triggers the shape change.

Viruses that have the power

Angela Belcher and her colleagues at MIT have used a virus to help them make a better battery! The virus was called M13, which consists of a long, thin spiral of protein surrounding a straight piece of DNA. By genetically modifying the virus to add some additional chemical groups to the helical protein, and then bathing the particles in cobalt oxide and gold, the researchers were able to produce high-efficiency electrodes which improved the performance of a lithium battery to twice that achievable with conventional electrodes made of carbon.

New joint replacement: hip and trendy

Biomedical engineers at Leeds University have designed a new kind of hip replacement which, they claim, should last longer than present designs. Most current artificial hips have a metal head which plugs into either a plastic or a metal socket. The continuous rubbing action between the two surfaces wears away the prosthesis and also grinds out small particles that are toxic to the bone that anchors the artificial joint in place, making it work loose. This means that up to one in ten hip replacements needs follow-up surgery to correct for the effects of this wear and tear. The Leeds team, led by biomedical engineer Professor John Fisher, is seeking to overcome these difficulties with a new prosthesis comprising a ceramic head inserted into a metal socket. The new device produces far less metal debris, which means it should last longer than existing hip replacements.

Hair-cell restoration – but not for baldness

Researchers in the USA have found a gene that might hold the key to regenerating the delicate hair-like cells in the inner ear which make hearing possible but cause deafness if they are damaged. Zheng-Yi Chen and colleagues from the Massachusetts General Hospital began by pinpointing all the genes that are active in the ear of a developing embryo. One of the genes they spotted, called called Rb1, the retinoblastoma gene, seemed to switch off the production of the crucial hair cells, presumably when the right number had been made.

Under normal circumstances these hair cells pick up the vibrations made by sound waves hitting the eardrum and turn them into electrical signals that the brain can comprehend. But as we age, or if we are exposed to loud noises over long periods of time, the hair cells decline in number and are not replaced, causing deafness. But when the researchers cultured cells that had been altered to lack the Rb1 gene, they found that the cells divided, producing many new hair cells. If they then added the Rb1 gene, the production of new cells stopped.

This suggests that if a way could be found to switch off the Rb1 gene temporarily in the ears of people with hearing problems, it might be possible for them to develop new hair cells to replace the ones they have lost, restoring their hearing. Unfortunately, the Rb1 gene is also known as a tumour-suppressor: it stops cells growing out of control, so cancer may result if it is damaged (or, indeed, switched off). The researchers would therefore have to find a very precise way to switch off the gene temporarily in just the ear-hair cells.

FACTOID:

'Owls can rotate their heads all the way round: a full 360 degrees.'

FALSE

They can turn their heads only through 270 degrees – but that's still three-quarters of a full turn!

ASTRONOMY

Star leaving the galaxy

Astronomers have spotted a star, which they are calling 'the outcast', leaving the Milky Way galaxy. The first of its type ever seen, it is travelling at over 2.5 million kilometres per hour. Scientists think that it is the sole survivor of a pair of stars that twirled around each other close to the rim of a black hole at the centre of the galaxy. While its partner was swallowed by the black hole, the survivor was flung out, slingshot-style, towards the edge of the galaxy. According to Warren Brown, one of the team from the Harvard-Smithsonian Center for Astrophysics who discovered the star (which is officially known as SDSS

J090745.0+024507), it is now about 195,000 light-years away from Earth. In another hundred million years or so, it will reach the edge of the galaxy and depart on a lonely course across intergalactic space.

The human equivalent of a chameleon?

University of Connecticut researchers have come up with a new weavable polymer that changes colour at the flick of a switch, theoretically ushering in a new range of knittable and washable textiles that will be able to alter their colour or pattern to suit the wearer's needs or mood. Just as in a normal fabric, Professor Greg Sotzing's 'electrochromic' polymers contain electrons which soak up lights of different wavelengths to give the material its colour. But when an electrical current is applied, the energy levels of these electrons can be altered so that they absorb light of different wavelengths, changing the colour of the strand. By stitching the threads into a garment, and linking them with microscopic wires to a controller unit, the criss-crossing strands can create the fabric equivalent of a TV screen, dividing the material into a series of small coloured pixels. And by hooking the controller up to a camera capable of imaging the surroundings, the garment could literally blend into the background, like a form of camouflage.

The team makes the new polymer by spraying it out of an electrically charged nozzle. As soon as the threads leave the nozzle the solvent in which they are dissolved evaporates, and the individual strands plait themselves together like a piece of rope. At this stage the researchers then chemically bond carbon and sulphur groups to the strands before adding an oxidant which cross-links them together. It is this latter process that gives the strands their colour and electrochromic behaviour.

But don't rush out expecting to buy your chameleon suit just yet, because there are still a few problems that have to be ironed out. At present, for instance, the colour range is distinctly limited.

How do insects pick up the pheromonal message?

Researchers at the University of Texas have pieced together the workings of insect pheromones – the chemical signals that these animals use to attract mates, and that control colonising and feeding behaviour. Insects pick up the presence of pheromones with their antennae, but exactly how the antennae detect and react to pheromones was poorly understood. It turns out, according to Dean Smith and his team, that these chemical messengers work rather like socialites on a match-making mission at a cocktail party. When pheromones bump into an insect's antennae they latch on to a locally produced substance called an olfactory binding protein (OPB) (one of which is rather appropriately named LUSH), and thrust it into the arms of a waiting receptor on a nearby nerve cell. This excites the nerve fibre and triggers a behavioural change.

The scientists hope that by developing chemicals that can interfere with this process it may be possible to produce 'baits' to attract insect pests into traps – which would help to control the spread of diseases like malaria – or repellents to prevent people from being bitten in the first place.

MEDICINE

The bandage that chemically kick-starts clotting

Scientists in the USA have come up with a new wound dressing that can simultaneously help to control bleeding and stop infection, saving vital minutes on the battle-field and potentially making the difference between life and death. University of Rhode Island researchers Martin Bide and Matthew Phaneuf have based their new material on a polyester – to give it elasticity – which is impregnated with the blood-clotting protein thrombin and with a broad-spectrum antibiotic called ciprofloxacin. When applied to a wound the thrombin activates the blood's clotting system, helping to control bleeding much more rapidly, while the antibiotic leaches into the tissue to mop up infection. The inventors hope that the speed with which the material can be used to control bleeding would free soldiers' hands to deal with other life-and-death issues. Off the battlefield there are many other applications for this sort of advanced wound dressing, including use by explorers, climbers or people hiking in remote areas.

 FACTOID:

'The average person's heart pumps about five litres of blood a minute.'

TRUE

Although this figure can increase to between twenty-five and thirty litres (i.e. by five or six times) a minute during exercise.

A fatal dose of indigestion

US researchers have uncovered a new form of plant defence which deters hungry caterpillars – by giving them a fatal dose of indigestion. Penn State University's Dawn Luthe and her colleagues made the finding by studying insect-resistant strains of maize. They found that these plants produce an enzyme called maize insect resistance cysteine protease (Mir1-CP). Plants armed with this defence switch it on as soon as a caterpillar begins to eat. Once the enzyme gets inside the animal, the Mir1-CP attacks a structure called the peritrophic matrix, punching holes in it. This matrix is a mucous membrane that assists with the absorption of nutrients in the intestines of insects, and it also helps to keep out parasites and potential infecting micro-organisms. But when damaged by the plant protein the matrix becomes riddled with holes, rendering the affected caterpillar liable to infection and unable to absorb its food very effectively, thus also stunting its growth. Indeed, when the researchers fed caterpillars on maize cells that had been programmed to express Mir1-CP, they found that it retarded their growth by up to 70 per cent. The team suggests that producing GM crops that express high levels of this protein could have significant implications for cheap and effective ways to control insect pests globally.

Getting a back-scratch that hits the spot

Chimpanzees, like humans, know how to direct each other to hit the right spot during a back-scratch, it seems. Previously only humans were thought to use gestures to direct the behaviour of others, because to do so requires the recipient to be able to infer the signaller's meaning – an ability linked to cognitive capacity. But now Simone Pika from the University of St Andrews, together with John Mitani from the University of Michigan, has found evidence that, at least when it comes to a back-rub, wild chimps can do it too.

The researchers watched male chimpanzees grooming each other in the Kimbale National Park, Uganda. To direct a grooming partner to pay more attention to a neglected area, the chimp being groomed would scratch a certain spot on itself in an obvious and exaggerated manner. Most of the time the groomer would promptly start paying attention to precisely the spot the gesturer had just indicated. This form of referential communication, such as pointing to something in the environment with the expectation of a specific response from another, say the researchers, had previously been considered beyond the capability of non-human primates in the wild.

The hand-held Aids test

Researchers from Cornell University and the University of Albany, led by biophysicist James Turner, have described how they developed a prototype hand-held device that can perform a rapid Aids test. The gadget contains an array of electrodes coated with antibodies that recognise CD4, a surface marker found on the white blood cells targeted by HIV. When a drop of blood is added to the device, the antibodies lock on to any CD4 cells, altering the electrical properties of the electrodes. On the basis of the change in electrical activity the machine can predict how many cells are present and therefore whether a person is likely to need anti-HIV drugs.

No-entry sign for ants

Researchers at the University of Sheffield have discovered a chemical 'no-entry sign' which ants erect to keep their nest-mates on the right track. Previously it was thought that ants used only attractive signals to point the way to the best places to eat, but Elva Robinson and her colleagues have described how, while investigating these attractive signals, they accidentally stumbled upon the ant equivalent of a ROAD CLOSED sign. The ants use these signals to improve their foraging efficiency by preventing nest-mates from making fruitless detours.

High-res LCD screens

Most people will have noticed the revolution in computer-screen technology that has seen large space-hungry desktop monitors replaced with slimline liquid-crystal display (LCD) models. LCD screens don't just save space, they save power too, and produce far less heat, which also cuts down the need for air-conditioning in busy offices. Yet even though they can offer resolutions higher than 1900×1200 pixels, the image is still not up to the quality you get from a glossy magazine.

But now technologists at manufacturer Hewlett-Packard have come up with a new kind of LCD which, they say, can yield resolutions of 7000×5000 pixels and can also be scaled up to billboard size for roadside or city advertising.

LCD works by applying electricity to crystals

sandwiched between polarising filters which operate a bit like sunglasses. When the current flows, the crystals change their shape, altering the polarity of the light passing through them and making the pixel 'switch on'. But to keep each pixel active, electricity must be continuously supplied. By contrast, the new screens only need power to *change* their image. The inventors have found that when liquid crystals are placed in contact with tiny polymer 'posts', they naturally arrange themselves around the post in either a flat or a tilted orientation. Applying electricity to the crystals causes them to flip from the horizontal position to the tilted one or vice versa. But both positions are stable, so when the power is switched off, the crystals remain where they are and any displayed image is preserved. Each of the polymer 'posts' is smaller than one-thousandth of a millimetre, so several thousand of them can fit into the space of one pixel on a standard LCD screen, producing vastly superior resolution.

MEDICINE

Gene gives some a taste for fatty food

The French are well known for their fat-soaked cuisine, so it may be logical that a group of researchers from Dijon should have discovered a unique taste bud for fats.

Philippe Besnard and his colleagues at the University of Bourgogne in Dijon have pinpointed a receptor on the tongues of mice that is called CD36 and seems to make fatty things taste nice to these animals. Given a choice between plain water and water tainted with a fatty substance, normal mice prefer the lipid-spiked drink. But when the team used genetic techniques to disable the CD36 gene in a second group of mice, the animals' preference for the fatty drink disappeared.

The researchers suspect that humans also have CD36 receptors and that variations in their sensitivity might be connected to eating disorders and obesity. Intriguingly, in the mice, when fats lock on to this receptor they also trigger changes in the intestine, including the release of bile in preparation for digesting a fatty meal, even before the animals have swallowed a mouthful.

 FACTOID:

'The human eye blinks an average of one million times a year.'

FALSE

In fact, a person blinks 4.2 million times a year on average.

How effective is the cervical cancer vaccine?

The vaccines targeting the human papilloma virus (HPV) – the family of agents that causes cervical cancer – have been shown to provide long-term protection against the disease. The vaccines contain the outer shell of the virus and prime the immune system to produce antibodies capable of neutralising two of the highest-risk viral strains, types 16 and 18, before they can gain a toehold in the susceptible tissue in the cervix and then trigger cancer. Although they had previously been shown to produce strong immunity when first administered, it was not clear how long this protective effect might last.

To find out, Diane Harper and her team at the Dartmouth Medical School in New Hampshire, USA, followed up a group of 776 women who had been given either the active vaccine or a placebo nearly five years before. Among the women who received the active vaccine there was evidence of strong immunity to papilloma virus types 16 and 18 (those represented in the vaccine), and it was 100 per cent effective at preventing long-term (over twelve months) infection and pre-cancerous changes in the cervix associated with these two forms of the virus. The vaccine also cross-protected against disease related to other forms of HPV and was extremely safe.

Cervical cancer is the leading cause of death among women worldwide, largely because it is so common in the Third World. These results show that this vaccine will undoubtedly make a huge impact on women's health, especially in less developed countries that lack the infrastructure to deliver a screening programme.

BIOLOGY

E. coli cam

Chris Voigt and his colleagues at the University of California have produced the bacterial equivalent of a camera. The team added a gene similar to the one used in our own eyes to produce light-detecting chemicals, then coupled this light-sensing apparatus to a second gene to make the bacteria change colour whenever they were illuminated. Although this result is merely a proof of principle, Voigt points out that the system could readily be altered to make the light-sensitive bacteria produce a useful product – such as forms of plastic – so that very accurate structures could be formed, at the resolution of a single bacterium, at the flick of a switch (and light bulb).

Stem cells get racehorses recuperating faster

Researchers at the Royal Veterinary College have found that stem-cell therapy can help racehorses to recover from injuries more quickly. According to researcher Roger Smith, compared with conventional treatments of rest and gentle rehabilitation, when bone-marrow stem cells collected from a horse's sternum were multiplied in a laboratory dish and then injected into an injured tendon, they triggered much more rapid healing in the damaged tissue, a swifter return to the racecourse, and fewer injuries subsequently. The same approach might therefore be helpful in getting injured human athletes and sportsmen back on their feet more quickly.

MEDICINE

The drug that combats the marijuana munchies

It's well-known among cannabis users that the drug boosts appetite. That is because the hypothalamus, the part of the brain that sits above the roof of the mouth and, appropriately enough, controls hunger, is sensitive to cannabinoids, the active substances present in marijuana. Nerve cells in the hypothalamus have CB1 receptors, which are rather like docking stations for marijuana-like chemicals, including a substance called anadamide, which are produced naturally in the brain. When these chemicals lock on to the receptors, they instruct the nerve cell to trigger hunger pangs.

The French company Sanofi-Aventis has now come up with a drug called rimonabant (and marketed under the brand name Acomplia) that can block these receptors, suppressing appetite and promoting weight loss. In a recent trial involving over 1500 significantly obese Europeans, those given the highest dose of the drug lost about eight kilograms (seventeen and a half pounds) in weight over a two-year period. Encouragingly, the study subjects also showed a 27 per cent increase in their levels of 'good' cholesterol. Only 50 per cent of this could be explained on the basis of their weight loss, suggesting that rimonabant might also have a beneficial effect on blood cholesterol levels and could therefore be useful for patients with diabetes.

However, in 2008, after the drug had been on the market for two years, reports of serious psychiatric side-effects and suicides among patients using the agent began to surface, prompting regulators to investigate. The drug was suspended while they conducted their enquiries. Since then Sanofi-Aventis, who also had high hopes for the drug as an aid to quitting smoking, have announced that they are discontinuing all clinical development of rimonabant. It may be, though, that new agents that work similarly but without the side-effects will be developed in the future.

Fit in body means fit in mind

Dutch researchers have found that exercise has a significant impact on brain power among the elderly. Boukje van Gelder and colleagues looked at data collected from 295 men born between 1900 and 1920, and monitored their levels of physical activity (including walking, cycling, gardening or other odd-jobs) and cognitive function for the ten years from 1990 to 2000. Men who dropped their level of physical activity showed a three-and-a-half-fold greater drop in brain power than men who remained active; men who increased their exercise levels showed no decline in their abilities. The researchers suggest that their study shows that keeping active in old age also helps the brain to remain fit, probably by boosting blood-flow and stimulating the birth of new nerve cells in the hippocampus, the part of the brain concerned with forming new memories.

FACTOID:

'At the age of five, virtually all children are able to repeat nursery rhymes, brush their own hair and teeth, do up and undo buttons, and blow their nose.'

FALSE

Fewer than 40 per cent of children at the age of five are sufficiently coordinated to blow their noses – most either forget to close their mouth or do not squeeze their nose at the right time. The majority just give up and use their sleeves, according to a survey. The same study found that the only skill more difficult to master is tying shoelaces, which most children do not manage until they are six.

BIOLOGY

The key to effective camouflage: highly contrasting colours

Researchers from Bristol University have confirmed why some animals' choices of 'camouflage' involve the use of highly conspicuous colours and markings – and it is for the same reason that military camouflage uses strongly contrasting colours. The colour clashes help to break up the outline of objects, making them harder to recognise.

To show that this is the case, researcher Martin Stevens cut moth-shaped triangles of card, with a worm for the edible 'body', and pinned them to trees. If the body disappeared they assumed that a bird had spotted the moth and turned it into lunch. The moths were camouflaged to different degrees with a pattern designed to resemble the oak-tree bark to which they were fixed. The researchers also compared the difference between patterns that reached the edge of the wings, and hence disrupted the surface outline, and those that did not.

Exactly as the theory predicts, moths decorated with the most striking colours which also reached the edges of the wings were spotted least often by birds. Following the theory, however, zebras should be practically invisible!

MICROBIOLOGY

The bacterial rivet gun

Scientists at the University of Geneva have discovered a bacterial toxin equipped with its own 'rivet gun' to help it punch holes in cell membranes.

One of the ways that bacteria cause disease is by poking holes in the walls of our cells and then soaking up the nutrients that flood out through the puncture. But while studying one of these toxins, called aerolysin, Gisou van der Groot noticed that it has a very unusual mechanism of anchoring itself to the target cell. The researchers identified a small fatty region at the tip of the toxin molecule which, when driven through a cell's membrane, abruptly changes its shape as soon as it hits the watery cell interior, and bends over into a hook. Seven of the toxin molecules all link together in a circle, just like a rivet. They form a pore through which the cell contents can leak into the jaws of the hungry bacterium lurking outside.

A comparison with other bacterial toxins shows that they too seem to use this rivet-like action, potentially highlighting a novel avenue by which scientists might combat bacterial infections.

MEDICINE

Stem cells for a broken heart?

Scientists at the University of Texas have helped to shed light on how stem cells can help to repair damaged hearts. Edward Yeh and his colleagues injected human stem cells into mice with heart disease and used the cell's 'human fingerprint' to track where they went. They found that some of the stem cells turned into muscle and linked up with the mouse's own heart-muscle cells, essentially wiring themselves into the heartbeat, while others turned into specialised cells capable of producing new blood vessels. The researchers also found that the stem cells were still working in the mouse heart a year after being injected – which is a long time in the lifetime of a mouse. This suggests that stem-cell therapies could aid in repairing broken human hearts, too.

BIOLOGY

When cross-dressing has its advantages

Researchers studying the giant Australian cuttlefish have found that males of the species often successfully resort to the marine equivalent of cross-dressing to father offspring. According to study author Dr Roger Hanlon, from the Marine Resources Center in Massachusetts, during the mating season fertile females are usually jealously guarded by large males, preventing smaller males from getting a look-in. So the smaller animals often disguise themselves as females, by changing colour and arranging their tentacles in a more feminine fashion, in order to slip past the male consorts lurking near by. Two out of three of the subsequent matings apparently result in successful fertilisation, showing that, with sex, deception sometimes works.

Turning the spotlight on microbes

A team of scientists led by Professor Luis Garcia-Rubio from the University of South Florida has developed a miniaturised sensor that can non-invasively detect the presence of infectious diseases using as little as a single drop of liquid. The new biosensors recognise the characteristic 'fingerprint' spectrum produced when light shines on different microbes. Because different organisms absorb and scatter light differently, the pattern produced when a sample is analysed can be compared with a catalogue of known infections to identify the bugs that are present.

The sensors, which can be used to analyse blood samples or to check the purity of drinking water, are capable of picking up the parasites that cause malaria, the virus that causes dengue fever and common microbial causes of intestinal infections and dysentery, including *Salmonella*, *E. coli*, *Shigella* and *Cryptosporidium*. It can also identify anthrax, making the system attractive to anti-terrorism squads.

Once a sample is placed on the sensor, the data is

271

transmitted wirelessly to a remote location for analysis, meaning that the system, which is currently undergoing field trials, is highly portable. The inventors hope that it will help to tackle the problem of waterborne illnesses, which claim two million lives each year, most of them children's, due to the fact that only one-sixth of the world's population has access to clean water. Rapid diagnosis of pathogenic illnesses could also help to stem the spread of diseases following environmental disasters such as tsunamis and earthquakes.

Genes that repel mosquitoes

Why is it that some people are eaten alive by mosquitoes, whereas others escape unscathed? It might be because, to a mosquito at least, some of us smell better than others. Suspecting that some individuals might produce natural mosquito repellents, John Pickett and his colleagues at Rothamsted Research in Harpenden first identified groups of people whom mosquitoes seem to avoid. They then collected samples of 'total body odour' from each person, enabling them to home in on eleven key chemicals that have the strongest mosquito-repelling action. To isolate the smells, the scientists used a Y-shaped piece of apparatus which gives mosquitoes the option of flying towards or away from different odours present in the arms of the Y.

At the same time, working with scientists in Denmark, they have found a substance produced by some cows, called 6-methyl-5-heptene-2-one, which wards off flies from around the herd. The research team is now in the process of patenting the chemical compounds they have uncovered, with the aim of using them to produce more effective mosquito-repellent sprays and lotions.

A laser-powered corkscrew to unblock arteries

US researchers have developed a laser-activated corkscrew which can be threaded into blood clots that have blocked arteries and then remove them. The system relies on 'shape-memory polymers' or SMPs (see also page 199), which can revert to a pre-programmed shape when laser light of the correct wavelength shines upon them. Duncan Maitland and his colleagues from the Lawrence Livermore National Laboratory in California have described how, using a model of the carotid artery in the neck, their thin polymer, which is initially straight, can be used to penetrate a clot that has blocked an artery. A quick blast of laser light locally then transforms the polymer to its corkscrew shape, enabling it to snare the offending blood clot, which can then be withdrawn from the blocked artery, restoring blood-flow. At the moment doctors often use clot-busting therapies to dissolve obstructions, but these can be costly and carry a high risk of subsequent bleeding. The Livermore team hopes that its approach will provide a cheaper and more effective alternative which may be usable in a larger number of patients and carry fewer side-effects.

FACTOID:

'Human children have more bones than human adults.'

TRUE

Children have 300 bones, but as they grow, some of the bones fuse together, resulting in a total of only 206 in adults.

ASTRONOMY

How fast is Saturn spinning?

Measuring the length of a day on Saturn – in other words, how fast the gas-giant is turning – has always been a problem for space scientists. As NASA researcher Giacomo

Giampieri puts it, 'It's like trying to tell whether an unmarked CD is spinning in the CD player: without some kind of marking on the surface – like a label – you can't tell.' And that has been the difficulty: you just cannot tell by eye how rapidly an amorphous mass of gas is rotating.

But now researchers think they have cracked the problem. The answer is ten hours and forty-seven minutes, and it will help scientists to model more accurately how Saturn formed in the first place, and how it comes to have the biggest equitorial bulge around its middle of all the planets in the solar system.

So how did they arrive at that answer? The *Cassini* probe, which is in orbit around the planet, has helped. Since its arrival around Saturn in July 2004 the probe has been making readings of the planet's magnetic field. By analysing this data the team was able to pinpoint a small but regular signature – a blip – in the magnetic field. By measuring how frequently the blip cropped up, the researchers deduced the spin rate of Saturn.

TECHNOLOGY

Will a sea wall full of holes hold water?

German manufacturing giant BASF has developed a clever way to protect sea walls from the incessant abuse of the sea – by coating them with a thick polymer layer that is peppered with holes. Strange as this may seem, there is method in the madness. The spray-on treatment, which is marketed as Elastocoast, has been tested successfully in a number of locations, including against the ravages of the North Sea on the 'disappearing' Danish island of Sylt and in north-west Germany. It is administered by mixing two chemicals, an isocyanate and a polyol. The polyurethane mixture hardens in twenty minutes, making it perfect for use between tides, although it will set underwater if necessary. A high-pressure spray applies the mixture to stone surfaces, or it can be mixed with loose stones and sprayed in layers up to thirty centimetres thick. But, critically, it is not a solid layer. The surface is punctuated with large pores a few centimetres across. When a wave slams into the surface, some of the energy is dissipated by the natural elasticity of the material. But even more is mopped up by the pores as sea water tries to force its way through, turning destructive wave energy into heat and noise. According to project leader Marcus Leberfinger, a wall reinforced with the coating has 'reliably withstood the huge impact of the waves during this past storm season'. Apparently the porous plastic is also proving popular with wildlife, the holes making ideal homes for crabs, limpets and shore plants.

A complete course of injections, but all in one go

A new system developed at Ghent University in Belgium involves packaging drugs into tiny self-rupturing capsules which are also pre-loaded with water-absorbing molecules called dextrans and surrounded by an outer polymer coating which is permeable to water but not to the drug inside. The drug capsules are then injected under the surface of the skin.

Over time, water oozes into the capsules and dissolves links in the dextrans, causing them to swell, which eventually pops the capsule and discharges the drug contents. The time it takes each capsule to burst open, which can be varied from days to months, is controlled by altering the number of links in the dextrans, determining the rate at which it swells.

Stefaan de Smedt, the inventor, suggests that the new system could be especially useful for people living in the developing world, where frequent or return visits to a doctor for a course of therapy are impractical.

Caterpillars immune to cocaine

One strategy mooted to deal with Colombia's cocaine industry is to unleash an army of hungry caterpillars. It is proposed to breed thousands of *Eloria noyesi* moths, natural Andean inhabitants, and release them into the main coca-growing areas, where they will make straight for the coca plants and lay eggs all over the leaves. Within a week the eggs will hatch into caterpillars that will devour the foliage, destroying the plants. The insects are particularly suitable for this task since recent research has shown that their nervous systems have a variant of the chemical transporter system normally targeted by cocaine, making them invulnerable to the drug. The only slight fly (or moth) in the ointment is that the Colombian government is resistant to such ideas on environmental grounds.

Hitting cancers where it hurts

Scientists in Australia have developed minute nano-capsules which can be used to deliver anti-cancer drugs to tumours, sparing other healthy tissue from side-effects. The capsules, which measure about half a micron – or a two-thousandth of a millimetre – in diameter, can be coated with an antibody that directs them from the bloodstream to a tumour. Once they are in the tumour, a quick blast with a harmless skin-penetrating laser producing near-infrared light causes the capsules to open up, discharging their contents. To make them, Frank Caruso and his team from the University of Melbourne have engineered a polymer which they add to a suspension of drug particles so that the polymer forms a sphere enclosing the drug, several layers thick. They then add tiny gold particles measuring six nanometres – six millionths of a millimetre – across, which stick on to the surface of the polymer, rather like the speckles on a bird's egg. These gold particles are sensitive to the laser light and allow the capsules to deploy their drug cargo at the desired time. When near-infrared light hits the gold spots, they melt instantaneously, rupturing the capsule without harming the contents.

The outermost layer of the nano-capsules consists of a fatty (lipid) layer to which a variety of antibodies can be attached to help target the capsules to specific tumours. So far the researchers have tested the technique using a simple enzyme called lysozyme without any loss of activity from the enzyme when it was released from the capsule. Caruso and his team are now working on testing the stability of the capsule in the bloodstream to make sure it does not break down before it reaches the tumour. At the same time, in a separate project, they have been looking at the possibility of using their system to deliver life-prolonging drugs to the nerve cells of the inner ear.

So apes can plan for a rainy day too?

Scientists in Germany have found that the ability to plan ahead is not, as originally believed, peculiar to humans. Our great-ape relatives, including the distantly related orang-utans, seem to be able to do it too, proving that one of our most formidable mental abilities must have evolved early in our ancestry. Nicholas Mulcahy and Josep Call of the Leipzig Max Planck Institute have shown that both bonobos, which split away from humans about seven million years ago, and orang-utans, which split off about fourteen million years ago, are capable of picking up the correct selection of tools they might need to solve a future problem.

The researchers showed the animals an apparatus which required them to use a specific tool to retrieve a food or drink reward. Later the animals were placed in a different room with a selection of tools, one of which could be used to perform the task they had been shown previously. At this time they had the chance to pick up any tools they wanted. They were thereafter moved to a waiting room outside for between five minutes and fourteen hours, and then allowed into the room containing the apparatus. If they had the right tool, they could obtain their reward.

The results show that the apes selected, transported and saved a tool not because they immediately needed it, but because they had a good notion they might need it in future. This is very strong evidence that saving for a rainy day is not a uniquely human activity and contradicts the suggestion that such behaviour arose in hominids only over the last 2.5 million years.

In-vitro meat on the menu

Scientists from the USA and the Netherlands have come up with two new ways to produce edible cultured meat in the laboratory. Both derive from a system of growing muscle cells in thin sheets, which can then be stacked up to increase the overall thickness, or formed as a matrix of beads that would stretch with small changes in temperature. The mature cells can then be harvested and turned into a processed meat, rather like nuggets or hamburgers. The scientists point out that there are several important benefits to the technology, including reduced levels of artery-clogging fats, 'meats' that are vegetarian-friendly, and reduced emissions of greenhouse gases associated with rearing livestock.

FACTOID:

'You could power a town for a month with the energy in a single lightning bolt.'

FALSE

The average lightning bolt unleashes between one and ten billion joules of energy. But since an average household uses almost two billion joules of energy per month, and there are thousands of houses in a town, lightning power falls a long way short of supplying a town.

MEDICINE

Fertile and free of leukaemia

Unlike adult men, many young boys who develop leukaemias go on to make a full recovery with appropriate therapy. But the therapy destroys the 'germ' cells that produce sperm in the testes, rendering the patient infertile. Recently, working with mice, scientists have devised a method of removing these germ cells before therapy, then reinjecting them afterwards to restore fertility. However, the germ-cell samples were often contaminated with leukaemic cell 'stowaways' which triggered fresh disease when the germ cells were reimplanted. Now, though, Japanese researchers have found a way around the problem – by using a special technique called fluorescence-activated cell-sorting (FACS). This system uses a laser beam to sort cells into different groups according to colour-coded markers. So Osaka University's Kazutoshi Fujita added markers designed to identify just rogue white blood cells to testicular germ-cell samples taken from mice with leukaemia. The machine was told to pick out only the germ cells, and these were then implanted into mice that had previously been sterilised by chemotherapy. These mice regained their fertility and remained healthy. When the germ-cell samples were not sorted by the FACS machine and were instead implanted directly back into recipient mice, all of them developed leukaemia.

Clearly, further tests will be required to determine the safety of this method, but these results are encouraging and suggest that it may soon be possible to restore fertility to boys rendered infertile through chemotherapy.

Music to your ears? How red wine stops you going deaf

Health headlines are forever championing the benefits of red wine, and now it looks as though you might be able to add your hearing to the list of its protective effects. Two studies presented at an academic meeting in London have found that antioxidants such as those found in a fruity Shiraz can help to stave off damage to the delicate hair cells in the inner ear that turn sound waves into brain waves. But over a lifetime, lifestyle factors and drugs produce harmful substances called free radicals which damage these cells, reducing their numbers and leading to hearing loss in old age. So researchers wondered whether antioxidants might have a hearing-preserving effect.

Jochen Schacht from the University of Michigan Medical School gave patients receiving the antibiotic gentamicin, which is known to damage hearing, doses of the antioxidant salicylate alongside their antibiotics. At the end of the trial only 3 per cent of patients given gentamicin and salicylate developed hearing loss, compared with 13 per cent of those given the antibiotics and a placebo.

In the second study, Matti Anniko from the University

of Uppsala found that antioxidants could also reduce the severity of another ear disorder linked to hearing disruption: Ménière's disease.

Schacht points out that, although there is no formal evidence that antioxidants like those found in red wine can prevent age-related hearing loss, studies on rats fed a strict diet intended to minimise free-radical production showed considerably reduced hearing loss as they aged compared with rats fed the rodent equivalent of junk food. So there is every reason to think that boosting your antioxidant intake, including the resveratrol found in red wine, could help to keep you hearing well into old age. But do turn down the iPod a notch or two, too . . .

Highlighting security

Researchers at Imperial College, London, have shown that materials such as paper, plastic cards and product packaging have a surface structure that is as individually unique as a fingerprint. In fact, the chances of two surfaces having an identical surface 'barcode' of imperfections may be less than 1 in 1-followed-by-72-zeros! James Buchanan and his colleagues scanned the surfaces of materials with a laser and recorded the scatter pattern of light produced by each. Upon rescanning a few days later, after 'normal handling', their system was able to identify every single one without difficulty, even if pieces of paper had been screwed up or soaked in water and allowed to dry. They also point out that, better still, no modification of the present product is required to implement their security measure!

Body-snatching bacteria

Scientists at Nottingham University, together with their colleagues at the Max Planck Institute in Tübingen, Germany, are working on a potential living antibiotic – a predatory bacterium that hunts down and eats other bugs, but does not harm human cells.

Called *Bdellovibrio*, the bacterial predator uses chemical sensors to home in on its prey. It locks on to the surfaces of other bacteria, including the gut bug *E. coli*, using tiny bacterial grappling hooks called pili, and employs a cocktail of powerful enzymes to drill a hole in the cell wall of its prey. The body-snatching bacterium then squeezes inside the target bacterium, which remains alive while this is going on. Once inside, it seals over the hole and sets about digesting its prey from the inside, growing as it does so. Once the supply of nutrients runs out, the now much larger predator splits into between fifteen and sixty smaller versions of itself, which burst out from the dead husk of the bacterium and leave in search of fresh bacteria to eat.

Microbiologist Liz Sockett and her team are now analysing the DNA blueprint of the *Bdellovibrio* bacterium in order to find out how to make some of the chemicals that it uses so successfully to attack other bacteria. More exciting than that, they are also planning to try to use the bacterium itself as a living antibiotic capable of hunting down and killing infections. This seems plausible because it doesn't trigger serious reactions in animals and it cannot infect mammalian cells. And as soon as it ran out of bugs to eat, it would stop multiplying and could be killed off, perhaps by using a dose of a drug to which the bug has been pre-programmed to be especially sensitive.

MICROBIOLOGY

How yeasts stay one step ahead of the immune system – and make nice beer

US researcher Kevin Verstrepen and his colleagues have described the mechanisms used by fungi and yeasts to stay one step ahead of our immune system. The team, based at the Whitehead Institute in Cambridge,

Massachusetts, has found that, like movie shape-shifters, the surfaces of yeast cells – which are the parts recognised by the immune system – change frequently to avoid detection. They do this by increasing or decreasing like an accordion the lengths of repetitive pieces of DNA in the genes that control their surface appearance. As the genes become longer or shorter they can swap places with other nearby genes, which has the effect of altering the chemical composition of the surface of the cell and making it much more difficult for the immune system to recognise, explaining why fungal infections can be so difficult to eradicate.

 FACTOID:

'More tornadoes hit the UK than any other European country each year.'

TRUE

Yes, but that does not mean the UK gets very many. According to estimates made by Dr Nikolai Dotzek from the Institute for Atmospheric Physics, Oberpfaffenhofen, Germany, fifty twisters hit the UK annually. Despite rumours to the contrary, the UK is *not* part of the USA.

These inflating and deflating genes also hold the key to a cool, clear beer, because some of them control a family of surface anchor molecules that lock yeasts together and also help them to glue themselves on to surfaces. The key to a crystal-clear beer is a yeast in which these genes are highly active, so that they form clumps and settle out readily. Otherwise, you get a cloudy pint. Ugh!

BIOTECHNOLOGY

Landmine-clearing cress plants

Scientists in Denmark have produced a genetically modified cress plant that can detect landmines in soil. Carsten Meier and his colleagues from Aresa Biodetection, the company they have set up to develop the GM strain of *Arabidopsis thaliana* or Thale cress, have modified the plant to make it change colour from green to red when it grows near an unexploded mine.

Nitrogen dioxide released by the breakdown of TNT, the explosive used in 99 per cent of landmines, triggers the plant to produce anthocyanin, the naturally occurring plant pigment that colours beetroot and makes autumn leaves turn red. The colour change takes about three weeks to develop, although the scientists don't yet know how sensitive the cress is at detecting all the landmines in an area, and whether the technology will work in all types of soil. There are also concerns that open fields full of lush cress could attract livestock into the mined areas. However, with an estimated 110 million landmines claiming two thousand victims every week across seventy countries worldwide, and the best de-mining personnel capable of clearing just two square metres of land a day, Meier and his colleagues are confident that their genetically modified cress – seeds of which can be sown from aircraft flying over potentially affected areas – will make a significant contribution to the detection and clearance of mines, particularly from agricultural land. Their current goal is to make their plants grow larger, so that they are easier to spot.

MEDICINE

Sniffing out *Staph. aureus*

Working with doctors in Birmingham, scientists at the University of Warwick have developed an electronic 'nose' capable of sniffing out hospital superbug infections in a fraction of the time usually required for a traditional diagnosis. Surgeon David Morgan and engineer Ritaban Dutta's e-nose takes just fifteen minutes to identify the smell-fingerprint of *Staphylococcus aureus*, a major cause of hospital infections.

The machine, which is about the size of a pair of desk-top PCs and costs about £61,000, was trained to recognise the unique cocktail of volatile compounds produced by *Staph.* bacteria using nasal swabs collected from people known to carry the bug. When it was then tested on clinical samples collected from hospital patients with a range of different infections, the e-nose successfully picked up 96 per cent of the patients infected with *Staph.*

Although it cannot yet discriminate between the 'super-bug' MRSA (which is the methicillin-resistant strain of *Staph.*) and its less harmful counterparts, the researchers suggest that approaches like this can be used to prioritise samples that might contain MRSA, so that they can be diagnosed more quickly.

HUMAN BIOLOGY

How much can babies actually hear inside Mum?

Researchers in America have discovered that the unborn baby can probably hear a lot more of what we say than we thought previously. Ken Gerhardt and Robert Abrams from the University of Florida implanted a tiny micro-phone into the inner ear of a lamb developing inside its mother, and then played sixty-four recorded sentences on a loudspeaker near to the ewe. For comparison, they also placed microphones in the uterus and in the open air next to the sheep. They then asked thirty human adults to listen to the recordings from the various microphones and repeat what they heard. The volunteers understood all of the sentences recorded in the open air, about 70 per cent of the sentences recorded in the womb, and 30 per cent of the sentences recorded in the foetal sheep's inner ear. On the whole, the researchers found that low-frequency sounds were heard better than high-frequency ones. Lead researcher Gerhardt said that the intelligibility of sentences was 'actually much higher than we anticipated'. As for music, 'They're not going to hear the violins, but they will hear the drums,' said Gerhardt. This research is important because it has implications for babies born prematurely and placed in noisy baby units where there tend to be lots of high-pitched sounds to which a baby of that developmental age would not normally be exposed.

BIOTECHNOLOGY

Allergy-free prawns?

'Genetically modified prawns will soon be on the menu for people with seafood allergies,' announced a host of newspapers in 2003. Reports revealed that scientist

Sam Lehrer from Tulane University in New Orleans had identified the problem area in a protein called tropomyosin, which is responsible for triggering over 85 per cent of seafood allergies. By altering the structure of a small part of this muscle protein, he was able to stop it interacting with the antibodies that usually provoke allergic responses, suggesting that a GM prawn modified along the same lines could solve the allergy problem. Unfortunately, despite the fanfare, no allergen-free prawns have yet materialised, either in fishing nets or on people's plates, probably because no company is willing to take on the legal risk of testing and selling a GM product that also claims to be non-allergenic.

TECHNOLOGY

The miniature motor, just millimetres across

Scientists at Birmingham University have developed tiny engines only a few millimetres across that could one day replace standard batteries. Smaller than a fingernail, the miniature motors run on lighter-fuel and produce three hundred times more energy than a standard battery, which means that they can charge up laptops and mobile phones in a matter of seconds.

The new motors are also much more energy-efficient than normal batteries. According to the project leader, Dr Kyle Jiang, 'It takes two thousand times more energy to manufacture a battery than the battery dispenses. Soon everyone will be able to recharge their mobiles instantly using a shot of cigarette lighter-fuel.'

It is believed that the new motors could be on the market within six years. Their use could also be extended to a wide range of applications, including powering tiny spy cameras, miniature robots or micro-factories.

MEDICINE

Who thinks most about food, men or women?

They say the way to a man's heart is through his stomach, but it looks as if it might be time for a rethink. That's because researchers at the Institute of Psychiatry at King's College, London, using MRI brain scans, have found that when men and women are shown pictures of food, it is the women's brains that light up in anticipation, even if they aren't hungry.

Rudolf Uher and his colleagues studied eighteen male and female volunteers both when they were well fed and when they had fasted for twenty-four hours. During the trial the subjects were shown pictures of food, or even given food to eat, while researchers watched how their brains responded. In all cases a part of the brain called the occipitotemporal cortex lit up, but always more strongly in women than in men, irrespective of whether they had eaten or not. This part of the brain monitors how other brain regions, including those concerned with hunger or pleasure sensations, respond to food.

These findings show that the females in the study were engaging in more conscious thought and decision-making in response to the food stimuli presented by the researchers. But why? The researchers think it might be a learned response and lie in social pressure. Indeed, they are now looking at patients with eating disorders, 90 per cent of whom are women. They have found that when anorexic or bulimic females are presented with images of food, they show far more activity in the occipitotemporal region of the brain than healthy women, reflecting their increased sensitivity to food. The team also plans to look at obese individuals to see how they compare.

MEDICINE

Baby born by ovarian transplant

US doctors have described the case of a woman who has become the world's first mother to give birth following an ovarian transplant. Stephanie Yarber developed ovarian problems at the age of fourteen, which rendered her infertile. Egg donation proved ineffective, so at the age of twenty-four Stephanie turned to her identical twin sister, who already had three children, for help. Her twin, Melanie, agreed to donate one of her ovaries, which was implanted on to Stephanie's own ovarian tissue in 2004. Shortly afterwards she conceived normally, and in due course gave birth to a healthy baby girl.

There were no problems with tissue incompatibility because the two women are identical twins, and thus genetically identical. But more importantly, as the medical team pointed out, this result shows that it is possible to remove ovarian tissue and store it outside the body ('put it on ice') – for instance, while a woman is undergoing chemotherapy for cancer, or just to delay childbirth – and then reimplant it to restore full fertility.

WEATHER

Can a mobile phone function as a rain gauge?

Researchers in Israel have found that mobile-phone masts might be able to help weather forecasters monitor rainfall – but not in the way anybody might have expected. Hagit Messer and his colleagues at Tel Aviv University have shown that because water absorbs the microwave signals used by mobile-phone networks, masts have to compensate for rainy weather by upping their output power. Recording the masts' output can therefore provide a continuous moisture measurement.

In their trial, the method turned out to be more accurate than conventional radar measurements and nearly as good as the gold standard – a rain gauge. But although rain gauges are more accurate, they are costly and cannot provide the same coverage or continuous measurement that the mobile technology can offer.

In addition, it might be possible to extend the approach to monitor atmospheric pollution, including particulates, as well as other weather conditions such as fog, sleet and hail. That would not necessarily add to the accuracy of national weather forecasts but it could in time lead to sufficient quantities of data being gathered to add to information about local weather trends and directionality in a variety of weather circumstances.

ECOLOGY

Goose cooked by global warming

Migrating birds could be hit hard by global warming because it can cause them to arrive home too late after winter. Christiaan Both of the Netherlands Institute of Ecology monitored nine populations of pied flycatchers, which overwinter in Africa before returning to Europe in the spring to mate. But in 2005 warmer temperatures in Europe meant that the caterpillars the birds feed to their young emerged much earlier than normal and had all but disappeared by the time the birds arrived and began to breed. As a result, the populations of the birds in the areas where the effect was most marked declined by 90 per cent.

Laser golf. Whatever next?

A US company, Laser Link Golf, has developed a hand-held laser range-finding system which can accurately determine the distance to the flag. The shaver-sized device runs on a nine-volt battery. Pressing a trigger and pointing it at the flag in the hole down the fairway starts the device emitting pulses of laser light. These are bounced back by a small five-sided reflector mounted on top of the flag. The time taken for the reflection to return gives the distance from the hole, accurate to within one or two metres. So far the device is proving especially popular with caddies . . .

Could this be a planet like Earth?

Scientists at the Geneva Observatory in Switzerland have discovered three planets, similar in many ways to Earth, orbiting a star known as HD69830, which is forty-one light-years away and just visible in the night sky. The newly discovered Neptune-sized planets, which have been described by Christophe Lovis and his colleagues, mark the first time that scientists have been able to spot planets this small orbiting distant stars. The team used a system called the high-accuracy radial velocity planet searcher (HARPS) at the European Southern Observatory's telescope at La Silla, Chile, to study HD69830, which is about the same size as our sun but twice its age. The planets themselves are too small to see directly, but HARPS enabled the researchers to spot a wobble in the star's path through space, which could be produced only by the gravitational effects of a clutch of orbiting planets. The three bodies range from ten to eighteen times the size of Earth, are rocky and icy, and orbit their star in 9, 30 and 200 days, respectively. Intriguingly, the planet orbiting in 200 days is at a distance from the star referred to as the 'habitable zone', where conditions are likely to permit the existence of liquid water.

The discovery of HD69830 in any case marks the beginning of an era during which it is certain that the first Earth-like planets will be found orbiting distant stars.

Fixed by skin grafts from a foetus

Doctors in Switzerland have been able to use tissue engineered from a foetus as an alternative to skin grafts in eight children with serious burns. Patrick Hohlfeld and his colleagues from the University Hospital of Lausanne used a small skin sample from a terminated fourteen-week pregnancy to produce a large amount of artificial skin, which could be grafted on to injured skin in patients admitted to their hospital with burns. The foetal grafts resulted in rapid healing of the wound site without the need to harvest a skin graft from another part of the patient's body. A genetic test on a healed area carried out in one patient showed that the child's own skin had completely replaced the foetal tissue by the time the wound had closed.

Foetal skin – the use of which is controversial in many countries and banned altogether in others – is well known for its ability to heal rapidly and without scarring, suggesting that it has the capacity to produce the right cocktail of growth factors to promote normal tissue regeneration, which probably explains the success seen in the eight patients treated in this trial. It should perhaps be noted again that those patients were themselves children, not adults.

Police to listen out for speeding drivers

Speed-demon motorists watch out: the police may soon have a new weapon up their sleeves with which to trap you – and it works just by listening to the sound your car makes as it travels past a microphone. The novel trap technology, which is being developed by researchers at the University of Tennessee and Battelle Institute in Oak Ridge, relies on the Doppler effect – the way a sound alters in pitch as a moving object approaches and then passes the listener – to calculate the speed of passing vehicles. And because it relies only on a passive microphone, which eavesdrops silently on a car's engine note, motorists have no chance of being able to detect it and slam the brakes on to avoid a fine.

To prove that the idea works, the development team recorded the noises made by a number of moving vehicles and then calculated their speeds based on the Doppler shift of the sounds made in each case. The system was right to within a few per cent in thirty-two out of thirty-three of these trials. It can even work out how large an engine is by listening to the sounds of the pistons; and whether a vehicle is overloaded, by comparing the change in road speed relative to the change in engine load as the vehicle climbs an incline.

MEDICINE

Monitoring metabolic make-up

Researchers in London have come up with a robust way to predict how different drugs might affect different people. Called pharmaco-metabonomics, the method relies on little more than a splash of urine. Jeremy Nicholson and his team at Imperial College had been looking for a way to realise the dream of pharmaco-genomics, which is essentially medicine tailor-made to an individual's genetic make-up. But the problem with trying to study genes is that there are so many variations and combinations in the population, so it is extremely difficult to predict how they will all interact. Furthermore, just focusing on the genes a person is carrying is not the whole story either, because it ignores the effects of environmental influences, including what a person eats and drinks, and even what bacteria they are carrying in their intestines.

A better approach, argues Nicholson, is to look at body fluids – like urine – because the composition of these is determined by the interactions of all of a person's genes *and* the environment. In other words, the body produces its own 'chemical signature', which can in turn be used to predict how certain drugs will behave, or even to which illnesses a person might succumb.

To test the idea, the team at Imperial measured the urine of rats before and after a dose of paracetamol. By using a computer model to compare the pre-dose and post-dose urine profiles, the researchers were able to predict what would happen to the rats when the drug was administered. This approach should help to make drug trials safer – currently a matter of considerable discussion in the UK – and improve the effectiveness of the drug cocktails that doctors dish out to their patients.

MEDICINE

Erasable tattoos

The days of indelibly pledging your undying love for someone by tattooing his or her name across your forehead, only to regret it later, are finally over. Thankfully, for those tempted to have SHARON FOR EVER etched into their dermis, dermatologist Rox Anderson from the Massachusetts General Hospital in Boston has developed erasable tattoos. He has found a way to encapsulate tattoo dyes within tiny polymer beads measuring between one- and three-thousandths of a millimetre across. When these dye capsules are scratched into the skin they are picked up by skin cells, which then take on the colour of their encapsulated cargo, forming a tattoo. But if you decide subsequently that you don't like what you see, or if Sharon is superseded by Karen (or even Darren), a single blast with a laser can wipe the slate clean. It works because the laser breaks open the capsules, spilling the coloured contents that they contain, which are then absorbed and broken down.

This is a marked improvement on existing tattoo technology, which, in addition to using dyes that are also used in car paints and contain toxic chemicals such as heavy metals, can be removed only half of the time, and even then necessitate fairly aggressive laser treatments.

CHEMISTRY

From field to fuel tank

Researchers at Rutgers University in New Jersey have come up with a catalyst combination that might help to safeguard fuel supplies into the future. Alan Goldman and his colleagues have found a way to stitch together short hydrocarbon molecules, which come from coal, biomass or refinery waste products, to make longer chains that are perfect for diesel fuel.

To achieve this feat, which is known as alkane metathesis, the team has developed a pair of catalysts that work in tandem. The first knocks the hydrogens off one end of the short molecules, making them much more reactive, and the second then sticks the two pieces together to yield a longer-chain result. In some cases molecules of between ten and eighteen carbon atoms were produced. At the moment the catalysts are still under development and they are too inefficient to be used commercially, partly because they are unstable and break down under the high temperatures (175° Celsius) inside the reaction vessel. But with oil prices hitting the roof, supplies dwindling, and more cars than ever on the roads, a system that can turn plant waste into diesel – which this ultimately can – could rescue the petrochemical industry from an uncertain future.

Glow-torbike improves rider visibility

Japanese manufacturer Yamaha has come up with a way to make motorcycles that are safer and easier for other road users to see – by developing a new glow-in-the-dark film. The phosphorescent polymer soaks up ultraviolet rays from sunlight like an energy sponge. When the UV interacts with chemicals in the material, it temporarily catapults electrons to a higher energy state. After darkness falls, the electrons slowly drop back down to their former unexcited state, releasing the stored energy in the form of a soft glow. Yamaha have developed a vacuum process that can apply an even layer of the phosphorescent material over irregularly shaped fairings, engine covers and cowlings. But above all Yamaha is hoping that the new range of 'glow-torbikes' will make the roads safer for riders.

TECHNOLOGY

Laser scarecrow

An Israeli company, Dim Arizot Ltd, has come up with a novel way to keep birds off runways: by disorientating them with a laser. In a patent application, the designers describe a disco mirror globe on to which several laser sources shine, firing light out in all directions. The device apparently dissuades birds from making a landing in the vicinity but does not cause long-term harm. The risk that it might attract drunken revellers, convinced they've stumbled into an open-air disco, isn't mentioned, however.

Superbug-slaying chemical uncovered

Researchers in the USA have uncovered a new antibiotic compound which is effective against drug-resistant bacteria, including the notorious 'hospital superbug' MRSA. Jun Wang and Mike Soisson from Merck Research Laboratories in New Jersey have unveiled platensimycin, a small molecule naturally produced by the soil-dwelling bacterium *Streptomyces platensis*, which uses it to ward off the advances of other bacteria. Tests show that it is highly effective against what are called Gram-positive bacteria, including MRSA, and *Streptococci*, which cause skin infections, sore throats, earaches and pneumonia.

The drug works by throwing a molecular 'spanner' into the bacterial metabolic production line. It blocks the action of a series of enzymes called FabF/B and FabH, which make fatty acids that are critical for the bugs' survival, including those found in the cell wall. So far it has been tested on cultured bacteria and in mice with bacterial infections, where it showed considerable promise and was very well tolerated. The researchers are now looking for a way to extend the range of platensimycin to include also Gram-negative bacteria, such as *E. coli*, which are currently resistant, probably because they are able to pump the drug out of their cells before it can have an effect.

However, although this novel agent adds a promising new weapon to our dwindling antibiotic arsenal, the doses required to achieve therapeutic effects mean that it needs more optimisation before it can be moved into clinical trials.

Retinal implant to restore lost sight

Researcher Laxman Saggere of the University of Illinois at Chicago is endeavouring to develop a solar-powered retinal implant capable of squirting tiny amounts of nerve transmitter chemicals that can activate other cells in the retina, potentially restoring vision in people suffering from some forms of blindness. The prototype device consists of two components: a flexible silicon actuator disc 1.5 millimetres across and 15 microns thick; and an adjacent solar cell. When light hits the solar cell, it generates an electrical charge. This in turn passes into the piezoelectric material PZT, causing it to change shape and bend the actuator disc. In the future a reservoir containing the neuro-transmitter will be placed beneath the actuator so that the change in shape triggered by light will cause a small amount of transmitter to be sprayed on to a target retinal cell. By shrinking the device, and creating an array of multiple actuator 'pixels', it should be possible to recreate a version of the visual world and trigger retinal ganglion cells to transmit this information to the brain.

Inflamed risk of heart disease

A UK research team has developed a drug that could make a significant dent in the damage done by heart attacks and strokes. Mark Pepys of University College, London, and his colleagues have produced a substance called bis(phosphocholine)-hexane, which blocks a chemical found in the bloodstream called C-reactive peptide (CRP). When cells are damaged, by whatever process, CRP locks on to them and then activates a cascade of blood proteins called complement. This has a powerful pro-inflammatory effect, in order to help the body to get rid of diseased tissue. But, unfortunately, the immune system tends to be overzealous in its response, and nearby healthy tissues are also destroyed. This is so-called 'bystander damage', and in the case of a heart attack or stroke it leads to the death of large areas of healthy heart or brain tissue adjacent to the area directly affected by the disease process. This in turn leads to increased disability for the patient.

The new drug locks on to CRP and temporarily stops it from unleashing this devastating cascade, greatly reducing the scale of the damage. In tests on animals, the team found that it was safe and effective in preventing the damage normally triggered by CRP in a heart attack. Furthermore, it might also prove very useful in other inflammatory conditions, such as rheumatoid arthritis and inflammatory bowel disease. The researchers are now planning to set up clinical trials to determine whether the drug is as effective in humans.

INDEX